Modern Science and
Modern Man

BAMPTON LECTURES IN AMERICA · *Number 5*

DELIVERED AT COLUMBIA UNIVERSITY 1952

Modern Science and Modern Man

by JAMES B. CONANT

Columbia University Press, New York and London

Contents **41598**

*Modern Science and
Modern Man*

Science and Technology
in the Last Decade

A FEW WORDS may be in order at the outset to explain
why I have chosen the title "Modern Science and Modern
Man" for this series of four lectures. When I was honored
by the invitation to be the Bampton lecturer for 1952,
President Eisenhower expressed on behalf of the committee the hope that I would undertake to provide "some
understanding of the significance of recent developments
in the physical sciences." On my inquiring as to the
nature of the audience, I was assured that professional
philosophers and scientists would be conspicuous by
their absence. My exposition, if not aimed at the proverbial man-on-the-street, was to be directed to the equally
proverbial college graduate—the hypothetical individual
whom college presidents welcome each commencement
to the fellowship of educated men. Being thus assured
that I was not expected either to give an appraisal of

the impact of physics on metaphysics or a technical account of the inner workings of the atom, I gratefully
accepted the privilege of being a guest lecturer at Columbia University.

Under the terms of reference thus graciously arranged,
I was still left great latitude as to my choice of topics.
In my endeavors to narrow down a vast array of subjects
to a few that could be handled in a general fashion in
four lectures, I asked myself, what are the recent developments of physical science that are significant to those
young men and women now graduating from our colleges
and universities? To ask this question is to come up with
the trite answer in three words: the atomic bomb. Or if
you are more optimistic, with a variant, atomic energy.
Now admittedly it is extremely difficult today to make
an address without referring in some way to atomic
bombs; particularly so if the speaker, as in my case, has
been to some degree concerned with the development
of these weapons. Yet an exposition of the elementary
facts about nuclear physics or an appraisal of the military
possibilities of atomic bombs, or an estimate of the peaceful uses of atomic energy—surely this is not what is expected from a Bampton lecturer in 1952. The technological implications of recent developments in physics and
chemistry are certainly of the utmost importance, but a
popular exposition of them would not go to the heart of
the question that I raised. For advances in technology
are not a new phenomenon, and the addition of one more
source of energy, when viewed in the cool light of engineering analysis, appears unlikely to be revolutionary as

long as coal and oil last. As for warfare, that is a special subject; it would certainly be out of place for me to give here my standard address on "The Necessity for the Defense of Europe in the Atomic Age."

I propose to examine the cultural significance of what has been going on in science since, say, 1935. And by "cultural" I have in mind the whole social pattern of Western civilization. I have in mind far more than the modes of production, distribution, and communication; I wish to include in my survey the impact of modern science on the philosophic presuppositions of the average enlightened citizen of a modern democracy—on his ambitions, his hopes, his fears, his outlook on the world. So in a sense I shall relate physics to philosophy, but only by handling both subjects in a general fashion and viewing each from the point of view of a deeply troubled modern man.

During the last decade and a little more, the attitude of the American citizen towards science and scientists has undergone a profound change. At least that is the thesis of this first lecture. I have just spoken of modern man as being "deeply troubled." I judge few would challenge this statement nor the validity of the overtones of an alternative title I thought of suggesting for these lectures: science and the predicament of the intelligent citizen. Now the awesome nature of modern weapons, the deep division of the world, and the continued high tension in international situations may be the only causes of the trouble that disturbs the dream of the intelligent citizen. Certainly they account for a large share of his apprehension. The changed attitude of society to science may be basically caused by fear of the atomic bomb, but its manifestations ramify in many directions and appear in surprising ways. So much so that if, as I sincerely hope, ten or fifteen years from now this fear can be enormously diminished by international action, the old relations of society and science will *not* automatically reappear. Let me make it plain—I wish they would: I do not like the atomic age or any of its consequences. To learn to adjust to these consequences with charity and sanity is the chief spiritual problem of our time. Therefore, in considering what I have to say, please erase from your minds, if you can, the knowledge that we are assembled on a prime target and that a potential enemy is every year increasing his stockpile of atomic bombs and may well be improving his methods of delivery.

When you have obliterated all thoughts of war and destruction, let me ask you to contrast public reaction to the development of the atomic bomb with public reaction to the steam engine, the electric light and motor, the telephone, the automobile, and the airplane or, in our time, to radio and television. According to my reading of history, modern science first reached the walking and talking stage about 1700, and only about 1780 did it start growing into manhood. Therefore, an appreciation of the changes wrought by science and invention could hardly be older than the industrial revolution of the eighteenth century. But that it is certainly so old is indicated by a statement of Thomas Jefferson in 1818 which he wrote as chairman of the Commissioners for the University of Virginia. "It cannot be but that each generation succeeding to the knowledge acquired by all those who preceded it, adding to it their own acquisitions and discoveries, and handing the mass down for successive and constant accumulation, must advance the knowledge and well-being of mankind, not *infinitely*, as some have said, but *indefinitely*, and to a term which no one can fix and foresee." (Now comes the significant statement.) "Indeed, we need look back half a century, to times which many now living remember well, and see the wonderful advances in the sciences and arts which have been made within that period. Some of these have rendered the elements themselves subservient to the purposes of man, have harnessed them to the yoke of his labours, and effected the great blessings of moderating his own, of accomplishing what was beyond his feeble force, and extending the comforts of life to a much enlarged circle, to those who had before known its necessaries only. That these are not the vain dreams of sanguine hope, we have before our eyes real and living examples." [1]

Such praises and such hopes have been repeated every generation in the Western world since Jefferson's time. But popular credit throughout the nineteenth century went largely to the inventor, not to the scientist. This was particularly true in the United States but not much less so in Great Britain. Imperial Germany was the only nation where the physical scientist as scientist received something like his due. The fact that from 1800 to the

[1] *Report of the Rockfish Gap Commissioners.*

present, various writers were continually attempting to
right the balance by pointing out the significance of science as contrasted to invention is evidence for the correctness of my generalization. By and large, the scientist
in the nineteenth century was supposed to be concerned
only with discovering nature's laws; the inventor was
taking advantage of these discoveries for practical ends.
The attitude of James Clerk-Maxwell, the founder of the
electromagnetic theory of light, towards the inventor Alex-
ander Graham Bell was one of patronizing condescension.
(Clerk-Maxwell referred to Bell as "a speaker, who to
gain his private ends, has become an electrician.")
Professor Rowland of the Johns Hopkins University,
addressing his fellow physicists in 1879, said, "He who
makes two blades of grass grow where one grew before
is the benefactor of mankind; but he who obscurely
worked to find the laws of such growth is the intellectual
superior as well as the greater benefactor of the two."
The scientist looked down upon the inventor and the
inventor in turn was a bit contemptuous of the scientist;
so too were some of the men of business who backed
the inventors in successful enterprises.

In World War I, President Wilson appointed a con-
sulting board to assist the Navy. Thomas Edison was
the chairman; his appointment was widely acclaimed
by the press—the best brains would now be available
for the application of science to naval problems. The
solitary physicist on the board owed his appointment to
the fact that Edison in choosing his fellow board members had said to the President, "We might have one

mathematical fellow in case we have to calculate something out."

Another story illustrating the popular attitude towards science and invention in 1916 concerns chemists, not mathematicians or physicists. At the time of our entry into World War I, a representative of the American Chemical Society called on the Secretary of War, Newton Baker, and offered the service of the chemists in the conflict. He was thanked and asked to come back the next day. On so doing, he was told by the Secretary of War that while he appreciated the offer of the chemists, he found that it was unnecessary as he had looked into the matter and found the War Department already had *a* chemist.

By 1940 the scene had completely altered: science had moved into industry and, belatedly, even in the United States, industry had moved into science. The electrical, the chemical, and the pharmaceutical industries may be said to have led the way. The great research laboratories of the General Electric Company, the Bell Telephone Laboratory, and the DuPont Company may be mentioned as examples. Therefore, when in World War II it came to mobilizing technologists to assist the military forces, there could be no question but that the scientists as scientists would be called on by the government.

I have oversimplified the history of the last forty years; the National Research Council was established during World War I, and by this action the foundation was laid for a closer relation between science and the national government. Indeed, the National Academy of Science had been chartered by Congress during the War between the States. Science was not an outcast in this country, but even as late as 1917 it was primarily the inventor, not the scientist, who was looked to by the general public as being the prime mover of technology; he was the man who had changed our habits and made possible our new comforts; in other words, the inventor had conquered nature and put it to man's use.

From the end of World War I to the beginning of World War II, the relation of science to industry in the United States was changing at great speed. The development of the atomic bomb only demonstrated to the public what was already known to many industrialists, namely that the scientists had now become inventors. The fact that so many *scientists*, and I emphasize the word, had been concerned in this development that had both brought about an extraordinary new weapon and kindled hopes for future industrial revolutions impressed the people of the United States; not only the people of the United States but those of the entire world. The transition was complete; the scientist was no longer thought of as a man in an ivory tower, gradually unravelling the secrets of nature for his own spiritual satisfaction, but as a miracle-worker who like Watt or Edison before him could bring about tremendous transformations of man's relation to his material surroundings.

The changed status of the scientist, to my mind, is one of the major significant developments of the last decade. Another is the altered relation of many scientists to organized society, that is, the government. The development of the first atomic bomb introduced a novel and highly significant element into the complex relations between science and society. This was in part due to the revolutionary military potential of the weapon, to be sure; but the essence of the novelty, to my mind, is only secondarily a result of the physical consequences of Einstein's famous equation $E = mc^2$. To me, the fact of prime importance is this: in the period 1940 to 1945 a whole army of specialists was engaged in advancing science in a spectacular fashion and at the same time was developing a new weapon of great military power. This combined activity was a new social phenomenon; we are still struggling with its consequences.

To illustrate what I have in mind, let me contrast two enterprises about which I can speak from personal experience, the manufacture of a new poison "gas" in World War I and the production of the first atomic bomb. In the first case, even if the "gas" had been as effective a weapon as we who were concerned with its development then believed, the impact of this war work in 1917–1918 on chemistry would have been of no significance. Why? Because as in all the other cases of the application of science to war until 1945, the technical area of the new knowledge was small and easily circumscribed. Actually, the "gas" was shown by later animal experimentation to be of doubtful value, but even if it had had all the terrible characteristics we then dreamed of—high killing power, ability to penetrate all masks, no odor, complete stability —even then this discovery would have been easily accommodated within the nineteenth-century framework of peaceful international science. Only if in the process of discovering the new "gas" the chemists involved had unlocked a safe full of exciting new chemical facts would this military application of science have caused an appreciable reorientation of scientific attitudes or the attitude of society towards science.

Chemical warfare, radar, proximity fuses, underwater warfare, jet planes, new mines and missiles—all these developments depended on the special application of the publicly known facts and principles of physics and chemistry; what new scientific knowledge was gained in these military developments had no revolutionary consequences in relation to the forward march of science. How completely otherwise it was in the manufacture of the atomic bomb! No one could be sure that the phenomenon known as the "critical mass" was an experimental reality until a large-scale manufacturing operation was put into motion. In 1940 the physicists were in possession of the results of certain experiments with microscopic amounts of materials; they likewise held in their hands powerful theoretical concepts in the new field of nuclear physics and chemistry. By an enormous extrapolation they predicted the operation of atomic piles and the explosion of an atomic bomb. Most of these predictions, however, could not be tested by any large-scale laboratory experiments or even by the erection of small-scale pilot plants. The flowering of this whole new field of science was dependent on the expenditure of a large sum of taxpayers' money; this expenditure could be justified in the 1940's only in terms of the destructive power of a weapon required in a desperate global struggle. Thus a vast scientific activity was born as a war necessity; it was marked at its birth with a word hitherto the anathema of scientists—secrecy.

After the war was over, as much as was deemed impossible to keep secret was published in the Smyth report; over all the rest a ban of complete censorship was placed. The difficulties of such a situation need not be recounted here; nor the struggles to decide what was vital and what was not; nor the inevitable conflict between the presuppositions of the scientist and the government official. Who can judge the wisdom or lack of wisdom of those who made decisions about security regulations in the days immediately following the surrender of Japan? Few could then foresee the tensions of the divided world in which we now must live as best we can. In retrospect it all seems clearer now; one whole area of science was inherently different from the rest; applied nuclear physics and chemistry were wards of the national governments of every industrialized nation; here, at least, science, technology, and politics merged, though often the confluence was a turbulent and, at times, a muddy stream.

If some nineteenth-century scientist could come to earth, he would certainly be amazed at what has now occurred. Michael Faraday was presumably in a cynical mood, rare for him, when he replied to Gladstone's skeptical comment about his rudimentary electric motor—the little wire whirling around the magnet—"Someday you can tax it." But he could never have imagined a time when the governments of free nations would exercise a complete monopoly over similar embryonic bits of science or would prohibit publication of new advances in these sciences—in short, a time when the government would regard the whole matter as a national secret. If he had envisaged any such social phenomenon, he would have realized the consequences that were bound to follow, namely, complete failure of communication between the scientists involved in the secret undertaking and the general public, complete failure of scientists and engineers to discuss new proposals, and failure to have adequate appraisals of the significance of each year's advances.

The future of atomic energy for military and industrial purposes has now become a matter not only of national pride but also a matter of pride for politicians. Moscow announces that the Soviet Union is using atomic bombs to move mountains; few if any informed persons believe these stories; within Russia, of course, no one can even discuss such matters. From Argentina come strange stories of new sources of atomic energy; no one credits them, few discuss them; within that country, no skeptics appear to have raised their voices. All that you may attribute to the authoritarian rule of dictators, to the consequences of a totalitarian state, but the situation is not far different in North America or in Great Britain. We read in the press about the alleged first demonstration of atomic energy for industrial purposes, about future applications of atomic energy for military aircraft or naval vessels; we are told that this or that development is right around the corner. The officials of one nation make claims about the future prospects of industrial atomic power; those of another nation, about hydrogen bombs. The significant, new, and alarming fact is this: in the face of all such statements those who are competent to discuss such matters cannot do so because of security regulations. Those who have scientific ability and access to the technical facts must remain silent. Consequently the public is largely informed through statements by politicians only partially aware of their own distortion of the facts, certainly unconscious of the degree of uncertainty in their predictions. At times half-truths and necessarily ambiguous reports "leak" into newspaper columns: these are some of the methods by which the public is informed of the progress of applied nuclear physics. I can underline what I have been saying by making one bold statement based on twelve years of experience behind the veil of secrecy: It is impossible today or in the foreseeable future to have a frank, rational, searching discussion of the industrial uses of atomic energy. The general public might just as well stop reading anything in the papers about atomic energy or atomic bombs. By the nature of the case it is almost certain to be misleading.[2]

[2] To illustrate what I have in mind, suppose that in the next few years some one of the four national governments now admittedly developing atomic energy should announce the completion of a plant for the production of power for civilian use. Such an announcement would be front-page news with some such headlines as "First Atomic Energy Power Plant—Government of —— Wins the Race." This headline would be misleading. Any time in the last seven years the United States Atomic Energy Commission could have generated electric power by coupling an atomic pile to a steam plant operating with low temperature steam and coupling this in turn to a turbine and generator. Such an outfit would have produced electric power from atomic energy but at a fantastic cost.

There is no use in wringing one's hands about the situation. There is no use in trying to find a scapegoat for what has happened or in denouncing all secrecy and security regulations. The world being what it is today and is likely to be for a long time to come, secrecy and applied nuclear physics are words that must be joined together. But it is of the utmost importance that the general public understand the consequences of this union. Furthermore, it is important that the necessary curtain of secrecy not be extended any further than is required; above all, that it not be extended into branches of science far distant from nuclear physics. Advances in science are difficult within a secret national monopoly because necessarily its research is guarded from all but a few branches of the government. Secrecy and science are fundamentally antithetic propositions.

Let me contrast what I have just been saying with two other major developments in the application of science within the last ten years. Consider the revolution in fabrics that is taking place, and the use of the so-called

---

Whether or not an atomic power plant is producing power at a cost competitive with a coal- or oil-burning plant can only be determined by an engineering and cost-accounting analysis; these analyses are always subject to argument and, to be trustworthy, must be public. This would require the publication of such secret information as the cost of the nuclear fuel, the cost of the plant, and the details of the operation, including the handling of the radioactive waste products. That any government can make such information public in the foreseeable future is extremely doubtful. Without such information, any news story on atomic power would be at best meaningless and in all probability would be entirely misleading. (For a discussion of the factors affecting the development of atomic power for industrial purposes, see United States Atomic Energy Commission, *Report*, July, 1948, pp. 43–46.)

"miracle drugs" in surgery and medicine. The facts in both cases are so well known that I need only remind you of them here. Starting with a more or less accidental discovery made by a remarkable man, Wallace Carruthers, in the course of his investigation of the structure of substances of high molecular weight, the DuPont Company produced nylon. During the development the matter was a secret, but as soon as the fabric was on the market, essentially all the basic scientific facts were made available and protected by patents; I do not doubt that to a large degree the so-called "know how" was made known as well.

A new lead had been opened up by Carruthers' work, and it was not long before other fabrics were on the market and competing companies were in the business. Indeed, the whole development of synthetic plastics and synthetic fabrics in the last twenty or thirty years makes a fascinating story in itself. But there is nothing revolutionary in this chapter in applied science. If you will, it is a further application of the procedures used by the German chemists nearly a century ago when they manufactured the first synthetic dyes and, later, synthetic drugs.

How is all this different from what has gone on with atomic energy, you may ask. First, all the developments I have just described have been in private hands; second, the work was not kept secret (by its nature it could not be); and third, various competing companies have taken up the ideas. Indeed, I venture the opinion that if there had been an attempt at a government monopoly and secrecy, some of the new fabrics which are now coming on the market would have been produced very much later, if at all.

Let me, if I may, just refer to the story of the production of the first so-called miracle drug, penicillin. Here again there were no secrets except for a short time. During the war, the work on penicillin was as highly classified as that on the atomic bomb. But notice that the traditions of the medical sciences and the whole feeling of the world essentially made it impossible for any one nation to keep this secret. Therefore, almost as soon as the war was over, people all over the world began to work on this problem in many different ways. As a consequence, a series of antibiotics has been developed and enormous progress has been made in their application. This is an example of free international science. It impresses the public, but notice how rarely it is referred to by people speaking about science in general terms. Why? Because there is essentially no novelty in this procedure. For several generations now, people have come to expect medical scientists to produce better drugs and better surgical procedures. Public health and the advance of medicine are almost taken as a matter of course. Along with the public's feeling that the scientist has now turned inventor— an inventor of strange weapons—there goes the reassuring thought that the scientist has continued to help the physician to improve the art of healing. Of the importance of underlining this aspect of scientific work, I shall have more to say in my concluding lecture.

Now I should like to examine a little more closely the procedures employed by the scientists today in physics, in chemistry, in biology, and in the application of science for practical ends in the whole area of the natural sciences. If in so doing, I appear to be underlining the obvious, I hope I shall be forgiven; for although a discussion of the so-called scientific method is almost a standard topic in a university, what I have to say is so antithetical to much of the current doctrine that I venture to present it in some detail here.

It would be my thesis that those historians of science, and I might add philosophers as well, who emphasize that there is no such thing as *the* scientific method are doing a public service. To my mind, some of the oversimplified accounts of science and its workings to be found in the elementary texts in high schools, for example, are based on a fallacious reading of the history of physics, chemistry, and biology. I will not attempt to trace back the sources of what seems to some of us a set of erroneous conclusions. Let me rather present my own analysis of the nature of science, if I may.

In order to produce a straw man that I may knock down, let me quote a definition of the scientific method written some years ago in an elementary text of chemistry of which I am a joint author: "The scientific way of thinking requires the habit of facing reality quite unprejudiced by any earlier conceptions. Accurate observation and dependence upon experiments are the guiding principles. The watchword is not 'what does the book say about this or that, but let's try to find out for ourselves.'" Then follows an account of the steps in the process of finding out. Such accounts in many textbooks, including the one

I helped to write, usually run as follows: "Scientists col-
lect their facts by carefully observing what is happening.
They group them and try to interpret them in the light
of other facts that are already known. Then a scientist
sets up a theory or picture that will explain the newly
discovered facts, and finally he tests out his theory by
getting more data of a similar kind and comparing them
with the facts he got through the earlier experiments.
When his theory does not quite fit the facts, he must
modify it and at the same time verify the facts by getting
more data."

Another and more sophisticated account by a biologist
is entitled "Steps in the Scientific Method." Note the
use of the word "the" rather than the plural "scientific
methods." Here the steps are listed: "Recognize that an
indeterminate situation exists. This is a conflicting or
obscure situation demanding inquiry. Two, state the
problem in specific terms. Three, formulate a working
hypothesis. Four, devise a controlled method of investigation by observation . . . or by experimentation or
both. Five, gather and record the testimony or 'raw data.'
Six, transform these raw data into a statement having
meaning and significance. Seven, arrive at an assertion
which appears to be warranted. If the assertion is correct,
predictions may be made from it. Eight, unify the warranted assertion, if it proves to be new knowledge in science, with the body of knowledge already established."

The simplified account from my own elementary text-
book and the more sophisticated version of the biologist,
I have become convinced, serve only to confuse a layman.

The basic fault is a failure to distinguish between two closely related activities which together have made the history of science possible. As I now read the story of the advances that have been made in the natural sciences since the time of Galileo, what has happened is essentially this. An age-old process of inquiry by which artisans and skillful workers improved the methods of handling inanimate nature became gradually associated with the type of thinking up to then characteristic of mathematics. Another way of putting it is to say that two streams of human activity, separated until the sixteenth century, gradually came together. These were abstract reasoning, as represented by Euclidian geometry, and experimentation, as represented by the work of the metallurgists who over the generations had improved the methods of winning metals from the ores.

Closely related to abstract reasoning were the broad speculative ideas of philosophers about the nature of the universe: of these the Aristotelian picture was predominant in the Middle Ages. A rival conceptual scheme associated with the name of Democritus was never wholly lost to view. Those who followed this line of thought imagined that the world was composed of corpuscles or atoms.

The usual descriptions of "the scientific method" are descriptions actually of the very limited procedure by which a person can improve a particular practical art. Indeed, if we take any one of these descriptions, we can apply it to almost any practical problems that arise in this mechanized age at home. Take the eight steps so carefully set forth by the biologist and apply them to the failure of an electric light to go on in one's country house. Certainly there is an indeterminate situation—something is wrong. The problem can be stated in specific terms, namely, when I turn the switch, the light does not work. What can be found that can be changed in order to make the light work when I turn it on? As to the working hypotheses, the first one will perhaps be that the bulb is burned out. The method of investigation is obvious: you try replacing the bulb with another—and the controlled experiment here is to see that the other bulb does light in a proper socket—you arrive at an assertion that is warranted, and the new knowledge easily fits into what you had before. Or you know by experience that it is more likely that the fuse is blown out, in which case you formulate another working hypothesis and make the test by turning on another light on the same circuit. In short, much of the so-called scientific method consists of rational experimentation or well-ordered inquiry directed towards solving a specific practical problem.

Now more than one teacher has pointed out to his or her class that, after all, the scientific method can be applied to everyday life and has used examples such as I have given. But I think this form of exposition is really putting the cart before the horse. The point is that what the scientist does in his laboratory is simply to carry over, into another frame of reference, habits that go back to the caveman. We can imagine, for example, that one of our early ancestors tried the impact of fire on various kinds of minerals, probably starting from a chance observation, and so gradually evolved a process of making a metal from an ore.

All this information is conveniently called "empirical," which means essentially cookbook information. John Tyndall, in a famous address [3] of a popular nature on fermentation, wrote, "Hitherto the art and practice of the brewer have resembled those of the physician, both being founded on empirical observation." (And I am giving this quotation to define my use of the word "empirical.") "By this is meant the observation of facts apart from the principles which explain them, and which give the mind an intelligent mastery over them. The brewer learned from long experience the conditions, not the reasons, of success. But he had to contend, and has still to contend, against unexplained perplexities."

At the time Tyndall was writing one could say that the art of wine making and beer manufacture was empirical. The work of Pasteur and subsequent microbiologists and chemists has greatly lowered the degree of empiricism. Still, even today, there are many procedures in these industries which are simply based on experience and cannot be related to the concepts or theories of chemistry or biology. It is convenient to characterize a given practical art or a branch of science by assigning to it a degree of empiricism. If one wants to find an activity where the degree of empiricism is very low, I suggest turning to the work of the surveyor. Long ago the science of optics was developed so that it is possible to

[3] Published in *Essays on the Floating-Matter of the Air in Relation to Putrefaction and Infection* (London: Longmans and Co., 1881), p. 238.

calculate by mathematical formulas the shapes of mirrors and lenses and to construct the optical part of a surveyor's instruments. Furthermore, Euclidian geometry provides a mathematical framework for the observations of the surveyor. Therefore, one can say that the surveyor's work represents an applied science in which the degree of empiricism is essentially zero. At the other end of the scale I would put the labors of any excellent cook, for in spite of all our knowledge of the chemistry of proteins, fats, and carbohydrates, the recipe for a good sauce or a good dessert is still entirely empirical.

I shall use this idea of the degree of empiricism repeatedly throughout these lectures. I introduce it at this time in order to tie together the work of the scientist and the inventor. In the heyday of the inventor, which I regard as being the nineteenth century, the elements of science at his disposal were relatively rudimentary and he was able, operating with those and with the aid of very little mathematics or elaborate theory, to apply the new knowledge by a series of largely empirical procedures.

Earlier I was dwelling on the new and revolutionary aspects of the relation between society and science. I pointed out that the man in the street—the public at large—had come to see that the scientist is today taking the place of the inventor; that the "long-haired" professors who were elaborating highly abstruse mathematical theories had been able to play an important part in the extraordinary development of the atomic bomb. Also, people are beginning to realize that in other fields as well, the lowering of the degree of empiricism of which

I have just spoken, that is, the application of theory to practice, has paid enormous dividends in terms of actual control of inanimate nature. Many hours could be spent relating the story of modern chemistry or our triumphs in electricity which follow this same pattern. The discovery of Wallace Carruthers which led to nylon fabric, the story of the development of various electronic devices, including the new solid material as a substitute for a vacuum tube—all these would illustrate the same point.

In emphasizing the distinction between developments in which new theories have played an important part and those based on essentially empirical procedures, I have perhaps done less than justice to one change which has been going on during the whole period of the growth of modern science. We have learned that there are ways in which empirical procedures can be improved without the introduction of theory. We have, as it were, empirically improved empiricism. The inventor in the last century working in his attic might more or less erratically try first this procedure and then that in order to get a better way of carrying out a step in his process, for there was no one to criticize him; if his methods were far from being effective, that was no one's business but his own. But when invention was replaced by the work of scientists in laboratories, then self-criticism was replaced by group criticism. People learned that if a specific problem is to be solved as rapidly as possible, accurate observations of each experiment should be kept; furthermore, even in trial-and-error procedures there is a difference between well-ordered and disordered empiricism. Take the simple homely example of finding out what is wrong with the electric light; we can all imagine procedures which systematically test one limited working hypothesis and then another or helter-skelter methods of operating where the same trial is repeated several times to no purpose.

What is often defined as the scientific method is nothing more or less than an approximate description of a well-ordered, systematized empirical [4] inquiry. Now, systematized or well-ordered empirical inquiries are one element in the advance of science; the other element is the use of new concepts, new conceptual schemes that serve as working hypotheses on a grand scale. Only by the introduction of a theoretical element can the degree of empiricism be reduced. Only by the use of new ideas of broad significance has science advanced—such ideas as those embodied in Newton's laws, as the notion that the earth is surrounded by a sea of air which exerts pressure, that light is a vibratory motion in an all-pervading ether, that matter is composed of atoms that unite in definite proportions to form compounds. The essential element in the advance of modern science has been the curious interplay between such theoretical notions and the experimentation of the artisan; through such an interplay scientists have built up a fabric of interconnected concepts and conceptual schemes.

Without unduly laboring the obvious, let me repeat: by well-ordered empirical procedures it has been possible

[4] Any philosopher who happens to read these lectures will note that throughout I am using "empirical" and "empiricism" in a sense other than that to which he is accustomed; I am using these words as they are commonly employed by scientists (see p. 23).

to make great progress in the practical arts. Such procedures are still being used in almost all branches of applied science. In metallurgy and organic chemistry, for example, the degree of empiricism is still high, but the development of new concepts and wide conceptual schemes was essential to the progress of physics, chemistry, and biology in the last three hundred and fifty years. As these sciences became equipped with more and more satisfactory theories, the degree of empiricism in the arts related to these sciences diminished. As a consequence, in these practical endeavors it became more and more possible to attain the accuracy of prediction of such undertakings as those of the surveyor. The practical significance of the advance in theoretical science lies right here. The history of the last hundred and fifty years in particular shows what occurs when advances are made in pure science. New principles evolve which can be related to empirical observations; at that point it becomes possible to control with far greater accuracy than before what one is doing in the practical arts and to predict the outcome of a large-scale operation directed towards making a commercial product.

No better illustration of this can be found than in applied biology, the very field that John Tyndall was discussing. I referred to Tyndall's words which were concerned with the practical art of brewing. Explaining why the brewer could not proceed as long as his art was founded entirely upon empirical observations, he said, "But he had to contend and still has to contend against unexplained perplexities. Over and over again his care has been rendered nugatory; his beer has fallen into acidity or rottenness and disastrous losses have been sustained of which he has been unable to assign the cause. It is the hidden enemies against which the physician and the brewer have hitherto contended that recent researches are dragging into the light of day, thus preparing the way for their final extermination." These researches had been instituted by Louis Pasteur in his study of fermentation. He had shown that living microorganisms were the "hidden enemies" with which the brewer had contended without knowing it. This knowledge was the consequence of a bold working hypothesis on a grand scale by Pasteur, namely, that fermentation and putrefaction were the consequences of the growth of microorganisms. Armed with his theory, Pasteur reduced the degree of empiricism in the whole range of fermentation industries. We accept the working hypothesis of Pasteur today as an established principle; we base all our procedures for handling food on the assumption of its correctness. Furthermore, this theory or principle is basic to medicine and public health. One need elaborate no further on this example of what theory can do to practice.

Let me give a reverse case where the failure to have any satisfactory theory has led to surprising consequences. I refer to the question of the action of chemicals on living organisms. In spite of an enormous amount of experimentation by chemists in making new substances and pharmacologists in testing them on animals and on men, one can say that it is almost impossible to predict the action of a chemical substance of a given structure on a human being or on a microorganism. An adequate theory would enable one to write down the molecular architecture of a substance and from this structure predict the effect of the compound on a living organism. Such predictions are possible today only within very narrow limits and with very special classes of substances. And even here the correlation is essentially empirical—we have no broad, over-all theory of drug action. Only within the last half a dozen years has some glimmering of hope appeared that chemotherapy can become a science.

To recapitulate, the inventor was largely an empiricist; he continued the tradition of the ingenious artisan. His place today has largely been taken by teams of scientists and engineers. To a considerable degree they likewise operate empirically; but their procedures are well ordered and systematized; they are disciplined by experience. In almost every field into which theory has been introduced, the degree of empiricism has been lessened. The teams of scientists in industry and in medicine are engaged both in reducing further the degree of empiricism and in applying the theories of science as they now stand. All this has become an organized social undertaking. As a sociological phenomenon modern science deserves careful study. Agriculture, medicine, public health, and the production of raw materials and their processing in industry are all interpenetrated heavily by well-trained empiricists using modern instruments to assist their trial-and-error experimentations. For the most part their success in advancing science, that is to say, developing new theories and testing these theories by experiment, are publicly recorded. Scientific societies and scientific journals make this intercommunication possible. Destroy the social nature of scientific research in the sense of destroying the intercommunication of scientists, and the advance of science would almost cease. Recognizing this fact, one must ponder on the consequences of the vast sums of money now being spent on secret military research and development undertakings. One cannot help wondering how long a large fraction of our scientific manpower can be employed in this atypical scientific work without threatening the traditions that have made science possible.

The history of science demonstrates beyond a doubt that the really revolutionary and significant advances come not from empiricism but from new theories. The development of these theories, in turn, has in the past depended on free discussion of their consequences. How much can be accomplished behind a wall of secrecy remains to be determined. This wall represents public policy. I do not question its necessity in these grim years of rearmament. But it is essential that the public in free countries be aware constantly of its existence and understand the special conditions now imposed on some phases of an activity that industrialized societies can ill afford to damage: the advance of science. If this be fully realized, then the significance of one phase of the "recent developments in the physical sciences" can be better understood.

The Changing Scientific Scene
1900–1950

SCORES OF BOOKS and hundreds, perhaps thousands, of articles have been written in the last dozen years on a single topic that might be designated as "the philosophic implications of the recent revolution in physics." Yet I am inclined to think that the layman is far from clear as to what has occurred in physics that warrants the name of revolution; nor is he at all certain as to what the implications of modern science are for his own private hopes, fears, and ambitions. Indeed, even in the more rarefied atmosphere inhabited by mathematicians, logicians, epistemologists, and theoretical physicists there is far from complete agreement as to the relation of the concepts of modern physics to various world hypotheses that for generations have been the subject of speculation by philosophers. To the lay observer this much seems quite certain: something tremendously exciting has happened in the area we designate as physics; this something is a complex of unexpected experimental results obtained during the last fifty years together with startlingly new theoretical ideas that have been enormously fruitful. What has happened is only distantly related in terms of logic and history to the explosion of the first atomic bomb; yet to most people, including many scientists, the large-scale release of atomic energy accomplished since 1940 is a symbol of the new physics. A revolutionary weapon and the dream of a revolutionary future source of industrial power have become thoroughly entangled with what some believe to be a revolution in man's concept of the universe.

Of all the features of the changed scientific scene, the fact that matter can be annihilated seems to many non-scientists the most bizarre. The popular writers on this subject have let no occasion pass to emphasize that the destruction of Hiroshima was the consequence of the annihilation of a small amount of matter which was converted into the energy that laid waste a city. To some, the real disappearance of matter seems as disturbing as the loss of life and ruin of the city, for associated with the word "matter" in most people's minds is the word "reality."

As long ago as 1876 Professor P. G. Tait, lecturing on "Some Recent Advances in Physical Science," said, "The grand test of the reality of what we call matter, the proof that it has an objective existence, is its indestructibility and uncreatability,—if the term may be used,—by any process at the command of man." And describing how the chemist can count on exactly the same

amount of matter at the end of a series of chemical transformations as at the beginning, Tait concludes, *"This,
then,* is to be looked upon as the great test of the objective
reality of matter."

A careful analysis of his entire statement would show
that what he was excluding really was a capricious and
unpredictable disappearance or appearance of matter,
but the way he phrased the sentences I have quoted shows
how ready was even a philosophically minded physicist
to bet on the permanency of matter. He was expressing,
it seems to me, something like a popular definition. And
these popular definitions are of great importance in determining the philosophic outlook of a thoughtful man
or woman.

Among scientists the idea of converting matter into
energy evolved only slowly during the first quarter of the
twentieth century. First came the almost accidental discovery by Becquerel of radioactivity. Some sort of pene-
trating radiation similar to the recently discovered X rays
was apparently emitted from certain minerals. By 1903
the Curies had isolated radium, and by 1910 the spontaneous transmutation of certain radioactive elements
had been carefully studied and the disintegration products
—as some of the elements were then called—had been
fitted into the chemists' periodic table. One of the young
pioneers in this strange new chemistry was Frederick
Soddy. What he had to say about matter and energy is
of considerable interest in the light of what happened
some thirty years later. In a popular book published in
1912, he wrote as follows: "Of recent years radioactivity

has been traced to the spontaneous disintegration of certain atoms into parts which form lighter atoms. The energy evolved in this natural change puts into the shade every previously known example. Mass for mass, the most violent explosives we know, in which suddenly the atoms composing the molecule pellate, liberate scarcely a millionth part of the energy set free when atoms fly to pieces. The great difference between the two cases—between, that is, the most fundamental kind of material change known ten years ago and that known today—has opened up for science an entirely new horizon. Kinetic energy only is sensible and knowable. Potential energy may and does exist in matter to an extent even now scarcely capable of being grasped, but until the matter changes and its energy of position is converted into energy of motion, this energy is unknowable and unavailable." [1]

From Soddy's time to the starting of the first self-sustaining chain reaction in Chicago in 1943, a certain number of scientists from time to time kept returning to the idea of releasing vast amounts of energy by a process of transmutation of the elements. By 1920 most physicists were thinking in terms of the special theory of relativity. But it was not until after World War I, when Aston completed his study of the isotopes of the nonradioactive elements, that scientists began to speculate in terms of the transformation of mass into energy. By the 1920's, Einstein's theory, the facts of radioactivity, the discovery of isotopes, and the determination of the masses of the

[1] *Matter and Energy* (New York: Oxford University Press, 1912), pp. 143–44. Reprinted with permission of the publishers.

atoms of many "pure" elements all resulted in a consistent picture in which artificial transmutation was a real possibility. But even then prediction was in error in at least one respect.

I remember Aston's giving an account of his work on isotopes shortly after the close of World War I and commenting on the possibility of converting the elements at one extreme of the periodic table into those in the middle with the consequent loss of mass and the evolution of enormous amounts of energy. (The Einstein equation was used as a basis for his calculations.) The likelihood of such a transformation seemed to him remote (or so he implied) and then he said something to this effect, "If the way to do this is ever discovered, the event will probably be heralded by the advent of a new star." In other words, the energy release, he imagined, could not be controlled and all the atoms of the element in question would go off together and this planet—the earth—would explode into a ball of fire!

As to the probabilities of starting the release of the potential energy within the atom, the chances seemed slight, even after the first artificial transmutations carried on by Rutherford. These were brought about by bombarding certain elements with high-speed particles. But so much energy had to be put into the particle to give it sufficient speed to effect the transmutation and the "hits" were so rare that the net amount of energy released was negligible. Transmutation had been achieved, but the hopes of releasing energy by this process still seemed remote.

All this was changed by the discovery of a new particle, the neutron, by Chadwick in 1932, followed not long after by the epoch-making discoveries concerning uranium. All of which has been described in popular language so many times since 1945 as to fall in the category of common knowledge. Certainly I shall not attempt here another exposition of the discovery of the phenomenon of nuclear fission and its exploitation in the period 1940 to 1945.

Few outside a small circle of scientists became excited about the gradual acceptance of the notion that mass might be converted into energy or the conclusion that matter might be destroyed by a human act. Even the application of the new ideas of nuclear energy to astronomy, the explanation of the source of the sun's energy, which just preceded the outbreak of World War II— even this would not alone have impressed people with the idea that somehow the whole nature of the universe had changed. At all events, what may be called the cosmic use of the theories of nuclear physics was dwarfed by atomic bombs and atomic piles. "Seeing is believing" and there could be no doubt of what could be seen, at least through photographs, as to the reality of this unprecedented release of explosive power. Therefore, the most dramatic, if not the most significant, change in the scientific scene within the lifetime of many of us is the acceptance of the interconversion of matter and energy.

The cultural significance of the revolution in physics can perhaps be symbolized by the layman's reaction to

Einstein's famous formula $E = mc^2$. That matter disappears under certain circumstances and energy takes its place is not too difficult a conception to fit into a common sense framework; indeed, the notion of the conservation of matter despite a chemical change, such as combustion, is a relatively recent addition to our stock of prejudices; it seems to be belied every time we light a match! But what has the speed of light to do with the whole business? That is the disturbing question; or rather, the answer is disturbing, for the scientist must say to the inquirer, "I'm sorry but that comes out of the theory of relativity, and it's very difficult, if not impossible, to explain without quite a bit of physics and mathematics. I can't even give a decent hint about it; you'll have to take it on faith."

To which the reply might well be, "You scientists expect the rest of us to be satisfied with explanations of the universe that for us seem only scientific dogmas."

The role of scientific theories as explanations of the universe, whether or not they be explicable to the layman, is a subject I shall touch on later. Let me continue to sketch in the outline of the new physics. The interconversion of matter and energy will not be regarded by most physicists as the exciting part of what has occurred in the last thirty or forty years. Far more significant, they will say, is the new outlook as regards the nature of light and the quantitative formulation of its interaction with matter. For example, P. W. Bridgman has declared "that since the turn of the century the physicist has passed through what amounts to an intellectual crisis forced by the discovery of experimental facts of a sort which he had not previously envisaged, and which he would not even have thought possible." [2]

As Professor Bridgman's words make clear, we are concerned not with a spectacular advance in science, but apparently with a break in the continuity of a line of argumentation. It is fair to call what has occurred a revolution in scientific thought, for what has taken place is a changed attitude on the part of physicists. This change has been forced by a series of experimental findings that have confronted the scientist with a dilemma that would have been regarded as impossible seventy-five years ago. All this is quite different from a so-called revolutionary discovery like the discovery of radioactivity; it is more closely akin to the formulation of such epoch-making new concepts as those embodied in Newtonian mechanics or Darwin's theory of evolution. Yet some would probably maintain that the new physics is more of a revolution, represents more of a break with the past than has the introduction of any new theory in science since 1600. But in attempting to evaluate the lasting effect of a series of intellectual events, one must remember that, as a rule, an altered direction of thought appears more drastic to those who live through the period of transition than to their descendants. It is by no means clear how the revolution in physics of the first half of the twentieth century will be regarded by the historians of science in the twenty-first century.

To illustrate what seems to me the essence of the new

[2] P. W. Bridgman, "Philosophical Implications of Physics," in American Academy of Arts and Sciences, *Bulletin*, Vol. III, No. 5 (February, 1950).

departure in scientific thought, I am going to use an analogy. Let me ask you to consider not light, but heat, and to recall that somewhat more than a hundred years ago popular lecturers on science fascinated their audiences by demonstrating that heat was a "mode of motion." The notion of a subtle caloric fluid that flowed from hot bodies to cooler ones could be shown to be totally unnecessary; indeed, not only unnecessary but also quite incapable of accounting for a number of experimental results, such as the generation of heat by friction. Therefore, the caloric theory of heat which had been useful in its day was disproved and in its place was firmly established the concept that heat was associated with the motion of particles. Nevertheless, the caloric theory of heat has remained a useful pedagogic device. We still talk of the flow of heat and even set up mathematical expressions to formulate this flow as though there were a caloric fluid. Within a limited range of experimental facts in physics and chemistry, the caloric theory of heat is still the most convenient way of ordering these facts. Note that I said "limited range of facts," for it was the introduction of other experimental situations that destroyed the over-all usefulness of the notion of a caloric fluid. To retain this theory and yet account for all these new facts, one would have had to add arbitrary assumption to assumption. On the other hand, when the theory was discarded and heat formulated in terms of the motions of particles, a vast new set of possibilities opened up. In short, experiments settled conclusively, so we say, which one of two theories of heat was "true."

At the end of the last century the nature of light seemed to be as definitely settled as did the nature of heat. Light was an electromagnetic disturbance in all-pervading ether; it was a wave phenomenon. The older idea that light was corpuscular—a stream of bullets—had been destroyed, so it was said, by a certain set of famous experiments that proved that light was in fact undulatory. Then along came certain new experimental phenomena which were as difficult to fit into a wave theory of light as had been the older set to fit into the framework of the corpuscular theory. About 1910 a highly unsatisfactory situation had developed which could be summarized by saying that light is emitted and received as though it consisted of a stream of particles and it is transmitted as though it were a set of waves. To the scientists of forty years ago this was the equivalent of saying a box was both full and empty; it was impossible, so they maintained, for light to be both undulatory and corpuscular. The fact that this appeared to be the case could only be a temporary situation. It would surely be only a matter of time before a set of experiments would be devised that would resolve the difficulty, for such a sequence of events had occurred throughout the history of science.

One is tempted to say that what has happened in the last forty years is that physicists have learned to love a situation they once thought to be intolerable. It is as though their predecessors had been forced to retain the caloric fluid not only as a matter of convenience in formulating certain experiments, but also as a matter of necessity, and yet the evidence against the theory remained unshaken. Furthermore, it is as though their predecessors had decided that the very nature of energy and matter was such that it was impossible to decide for or against the two ideas of heat: the caloric theory or heat as a mode of motion. But such a decision on the part of early nineteenth-century scientists would have been a negation of science itself—at least, so people would have declared until very recent years. The progress of science consisted in testing the deductions from various hypotheses and discarding the hypothesis the deductions from which were contradicted by experiment. The idea that there could be two diametrically opposed theories as to the nature of heat, or of light, or of matter, and that both could be rejected and confirmed as a consequence of experiments would have been considered nonsense to almost all sane people fifty years ago. In regard to heat we can still agree that the caloric fluid is obsolete, make no mistake about that; in regard to light, however, we can hardly do better than say that light is in a sense both undulatory and corpuscular. In regard to matter, we have already seen that here too a certain ambiguity has entered in.

I do not propose in this series of lectures to attempt even to list the experimental findings that have brought about the revolution in physics. They are not few and are certainly not simple. Their interpretation is so closely interwoven with the new theoretical outlook as to make it extremely difficult to isolate single crucial experiments. Indeed, I think that a certain degree of caution is appropriate in reading some of the popular expositions of the implications of the new physics. For in simplifying a complex experiment, the writer is almost forced to intrude an interpretation before he draws the conclusion from the evidence.

At all events, it would be hopeless in a portion of one lecture to deal with a mass of experimental evidence that would require many lectures for even a summary review for a general audience.

My theme in this lecture, let me remind you, is the changed attitude of the public towards science and the altered viewpoint of the scientist towards science. As an illustration of the latter, a few words may be appropriate as to the twentieth-century fate of the two great principles of the nineteenth century: the conservation of mass and the conservation of energy. The atomic energy story has already made familiar the union of these two principles. We have now to consider the willingness of physicists to postulate the existence of a particle, the *neutrino*, for the sole purpose of balancing the mass-energy accounts on the two sides of the ledger in certain transformations in nuclear physics. To date, as far as I am aware, there is no experimental evidence for the existence of this particle, nor does it seem likely, I am told, that experimental tests can be devised to establish or disprove its existence. We have the choice of assuming that in certain experiments the conservation of mass and energy fails or that a neutrino is liberated. It is certainly far more convenient to choose the second alternative; the number of instances when this neutrino has to be postulated are few, and everywhere else the mass-energy relations hold within the accuracy of measurement. Therefore, the neutrino fulfills the same practical function as the caloric fluid once did and still does when we wish to analyze the flow of heat.

So far, I have emphasized the uncomfortable situations that have arisen as a consequence of the advance of science since the turn of the century. In an attempt to right the balance I must insert here a few words about the surprising way (surprising to some, at least) in which the theories of the chemist and the physicist have converged. That this would be the course of events was by no means certain in 1900. At that time the atomic-molecular theory of the chemists and the molecular theory of the physicists seemed to be only distantly related. The chemist had drawn pictures of the way atoms were arranged in space in certain molecules to account for a highly special set of experimental observations. More than one skeptic expressed doubts as to the reality of such molecular models. They were concepts which if true would account for the facts as then observed; this highly restricted statement was all that some would care to maintain. Before the half-century mark was passed, however, physicists studying an entirely different set of phenomena —the interaction of light (of short wave lengths, including X rays) and matter—came to conclusions identical with those of the chemists. Today, if one wishes to give the evidence in favor of a certain model for a complex molecule, the results of chemical and physical experiments will be intermingled and treated as of equal value.

In a word, the conceptual schemes of the chemist and the physicist as to the atomicity of matter, starting from entirely different observations, have come together.

Notice that it is conceivable that we might have had to be operating with two sets of models, one to assist the chemist in formulating the results of his labors, the other to guide the investigations of the physicists. To some of us forty years ago, such an eventuality seemed a likely outcome. We may therefore rejoice that the development has been in the contrary direction, that the two schemes are now essentially one. I say "rejoice," for quite apart from any metaphysical bias, it surely makes for simplicity and hence practicality to have only one set of atoms to deal with when we talk about the architecture of molecules.

While the experiments of the last few decades have led towards a simplification of the concept of molecules composed of atoms, the structure of the atom itself presents a complex and somewhat confusing picture. Again I shall attempt no exposition of the detailed experimental findings; instead, I shall only point out the general trend of current interpretations. Our desire for a simple picture of the universe was remarkably well satisfied a few years ago when it could be said that all atoms appeared to be composed of three kinds of building bricks: neutrons, protons, and electrons. The transmutation of elements in this scheme of things thus could be roughly pictured as analogous to the change of one compound into another; according to the atomic-molecular theory, one compound differs from another only in the number and kind of atoms grouped together in a molecule. In the generally employed picture of the inside of an atom, one element differs from another only in regard to the number of elementary particles of which the massive center of the atom (the nucleus) is composed. Almost any popular account of atomic energy will give a satisfying qualitative description of the structure of matter. The difference between one kind of uranium and another (that is, the concept of isotopes) can be readily pictured; likewise the spontaneous disintegration of the nucleus of the radioactive elements can be shown by diagrams far more simple than those required by the chemist to explain the difference between cane sugar and glucose, for example. (The picture is simple, let us remember, if we do not push too far our inquiry as to the relation of mass to energy and if we do not ask embarrassing questions about why the speed of light comes into Einstein's equation.)

The analogy between the architecture of molecules and that of atoms breaks down at a number of points. In the last half dozen years the difficulties that have arisen which make the simple picture more complex can be summarized in a few words: the number of elementary particles has multiplied in an embarrassing fashion. To oversimplify the situation, let me put it this way: if only neutrons, protons, and electrons were the building blocks of atoms, then all the disintegrations of atomic nuclei should yield only these particles in addition to other nuclei. (There would be a few exceptions to this statement; for example, the neutrino was introduced to take care of the conservation of mass and energy.) Experiments involving the interaction of matter and particles moving at extremely high speeds (and thus carrying great energy) have produced almost a swarm of new particles, certainly a half dozen. If one wishes to give as evidence for the proton-neutron-electron picture the production of these three particles in many spontaneous and artificial disintegrations, it is embarrassing to find so many other particles appearing when disintegrations are carried out under a somewhat different set of circumstances. Perhaps it is not correct to say that the atom contains any of these particles in the sense that a pillbox contains pills. Perhaps a better analogy is to be found in a piece of brittle candy which breaks into bits when it is struck with a hammer—perhaps all the particles are generated in the disintegration process rather than existing preformed in the nucleus of the atom. But, if so, why is there as much uniformity as we find? Why are there not different particles for every different disintegration process?

Questions like these—their sophisticated equivalents, it might be fair to say—raise doubts as to whether the conceptual scheme of nuclear physics is a "real" account of the structure of the universe. But similar doubts have not only been raised, they have also been proclaimed at the crossroads for twenty years by many (but not all) leading physicists and philosophers of science. Long before the growing complexity of the picture of the inside of the atom was manifest, these men were declaring that the new physics was revolutionary. And by revolutionary they had in mind an outlook altered in a totally unexpected manner.

One of the prime factors in changing the scientific point of view has been the failure to settle by experiment the validity of the wave theory versus the corpuscular theory of light. I have suggested earlier that the physicist has learned to live with a paradox that once seemed intolerable. It might be better to say that he has discovered how general is the paradox and by what mathematical manipulations of experimental data he can get forward with all manner of undertakings because of the paradox. If a layman persists today with the question: is a beam of light composed of particles or waves, he would probably receive an answer from most philosophically minded physicists somewhat as follows: "That is not a useful question. We physicists have stopped asking it; but if you insist, we may say that a beam of light is at one and the same time a set of particles and waves. But let us hasten to add, so is a beam of electrons or of rapidly moving atomic nuclei. Furthermore, lest you confuse the new physics with the mere failure of the old, let me make it plain that in our new conceptual scheme we can define mathematically our uncertainties as to the interaction of a stream of particles or waves with larger aggregates of matter. In short, there is a whole new branch of physics called quantum mechanics that now accommodates a vast amount of experimental material in both physics and chemistry and has been as fruitful as any development in the history of the physical sciences. So if the solidity of matter seems to have gone out from under you, don't for a moment think that this has impeded the advance of science, for quite the contrary is the case."

To give a hint as to the revolutionary nature of quantum mechanics (it is only a hint), let me deal not with the interaction of radiation and matter—the usual field for exposition of quantum phenomena—but with the modern picture of a molecule. Let us take a relatively simple substance such as carbon tetrachloride, the basis of many noninflammable cleaning fluids. Somewhat less than a century ago the chemists' atomic-molecular theory was developed to a point where people were agreed that carbon tetrachloride was best represented by assuming that each molecule contained a carbon atom surrounded by four chlorine atoms arranged more or less as a tetrahedron. Now, in 1952, we say we can locate, by means of the techniques of physics, the centers of the carbon atom and the four chlorine atoms—the atomic nuclei. But when we try to talk about where the electrons are that are somehow involved in the linkage of the carbon and chlorine atoms, then we are unable to be precise.

According to the picture we now draw, the five nuclei are positively charged, that of the carbon carrying four charges and each of the chlorine nuclei, seven. The carbon tetrachloride molecule is electrically neutral, so in some manner a total of $4 + (4 \times 7) = 32$ electrons are distributed around the five atomic centers. A generation ago, chemists were often engaged in speculating as to where these 32 electrons were located in the model of a molecule. The essence of the new quantum mechanics lies in the fact that we now say that one can never determine by any conceivable experiment the exact location of any of these electrons. There are various ways of formulating their distribution, the nature of which generates the forces holding the nuclei together, but only in a statistical sense can we describe the location of these so-called binding electrons.

The attempt to give some idea of the famous uncertainty principle by contrasting our certainty in locating atomic centers in molecules with our belief in the inherent uncertainty of the positions of the electrons may or may not be a suitable pedagogic device for this audience. But it does enable me to compare the new uncertainty of quantum mechanics with a somewhat older one that is involved in the kinetic theory of gases. The idea of a gas being composed of very small particles whose bulk occupies only a very small portion of the total space is a product of the first half of the nineteenth century. The picture of a gas as a swarm of fast-moving particles has inherent in it a statistical view of the whole scene. No one attempts to trace the course of a single molecule flying about and bouncing off the walls of the container or off other molecules, but it is possible to treat mathematically a large number of such particles. The resulting theory has proved to be one of the foundation stones of nineteenth-century physics and chemistry.

Now, most of the interpreters of modern quantum mechanics sharply differentiate between the uncertainty in regard to any single particle in a gas, according to the kinetic theory, and the uncertainty as to the position of a binding electron in a molecule. Some others, in attempting to popularize the altered outlook of the physicist, have on the contrary suggested that the two uncertainties, if not quite the same thing, are at least very similar. The reasons given by those who stress the peculiar nature of the uncertainty in regard to electrons are of special interest. They amount to this: that until quantum phenomena intruded themselves on physicists and quantum mechanics developed, scientists were convinced that *in principle* the motion of every particle could be calculated in advance. Now they are convinced that this is true only within certain limits defined by a mathematical equation. (And the equation is such that for very small objects like electrons, the inherent uncertainty is great.) Perhaps it would not be too far wrong to say that to the degree that scientists had subscribed to this "in principle" mechanical philosophy, the new quantum mechanics seems revolutionary.

Just what does the new outlook mean for those interested in constructing a total picture of the universe? Professor Bridgman has said, in considering the philosophical implications of physics:

"Finally, I come to what it seems to me may well be from the long range point of view the most revolutionary of the insights to be derived from our recent experiences in physics, more revolutionary than the insights afforded by the discoveries of Galileo and Newton, or of Darwin. This is the insight that it is impossible to transcend the human reference point. . . . The new insight comes from a realization that the structure of nature may eventually be such that our processes of thought do not correspond to it sufficiently to permit us to think about it all. We have already had an intimation of this in the behavior of very small things in the quantum domain . . . there can be no difference of opinion with regard to the dilemma that now confronts us in the direction of the very small. We are now approaching a bound beyond which we are forever estopped from pushing our inquiries, not by the construction of the world, but by the construction of ourselves. The world fades out and eludes us because it becomes meaningless. We cannot even express this in the way we would like. We cannot say that there exists a world beyond any knowledge possible to us because of the nature of knowledge. The very concept of existence becomes meaningless. It is literally true that the only way of reacting to this is to shut up. We are confronted with something truly ineffable. We have reached the limit of the vision of the great pioneers of science, the vision, namely that we live in a sympathetic world, in that it is comprehensible by our minds." [3]

Professor Dingle of London has written, "The men who carried on the scientific tradition established in the seventeenth century did so truly and faithfully, but thinking all the time that they were doing something else. The revolution that came in the twentieth century was simply the overthrow of the false notion of what science was and is; science itself has pursued the same undeviating course from Galileo through Newton and Einstein to our own time." [4]

[3] P. W. Bridgman, "Philosophical Implications of Physics," in American Academy of Arts and Sciences, *Bulletin*, Vol. III, No. 5 (February, 1950).
[4] Herbert Dingle, "The Scientific Outlook in 1851 and in 1951," *British Journal for the Philosophy of Science*, II (1951), 86.

"What the mid-nineteenth century scientists thought they were doing," Dingle goes on to say, was looking out "upon a real external substantial world of material bodies whose content was measured by its mass or weight. . . . The information thus provided gave clues—often very indirect—to the eternal and unchanging principles that were firmly believed to underlie the behaviour of the world. . . . The world was thus regarded as exhibiting, with the passage of time, a succession of states, each connected with its predecessor and successor by what were regarded as unbreakable links of absolute necessity. This was referred to as the principle of cause and effect. . . .

"In general terms we may say that the Victorians looked on the progress of science as a process of accumulation. . . . Our view today is very different . . . the picture of the whole which we form in our attempt to express its interrelations undergoes unceasing transformations. . . . We can no longer say, The World is like this, or the World is like that. We can only say, Our experience up to the present is best represented by a world of this character; I do not know what model will best represent the world of tomorrow, but I do know that it will coordinate a greater range of experience than that of today." [5]

According to this interpretation of the history of science, what nineteenth-century physicists thought they were doing was discovering the causal laws that governed the world of material substance; actually, to use Professor Dingle's words, "They were at little more than the begin-

[5] *Ibid.*, pp. 89, 98–99.

ning of their task of understanding the world of experience." Yet in contrasting the present with the past, it is important to note that not all nineteenth-century scientists were of one mind as to the nature of their task. One need only mention the name of Ernst Mach, whose point of view in our own time has led to the doctrines of the logical empiricists, to indicate that there were some skeptics in regard to the possibilities of determining once and for all the nature of the material universe. P. G. Tait in 1876 in his lectures on "Some Recent Advances in Physical Science" stated that "nothing is more preposterously unscientific than to assert (as is constantly done by the quasi-scientific writers of the present day) that with the utmost strides attempted by science we should necessarily be sensibly nearer to a conception of the ultimate nature of matter." Even as orthodox a physicist as J. J. Thomson reflected the same view when, in the introductory paragraphs to his little book *The Corpuscular Theory of Matter*, published in 1907, he stated that his new theory was not to be regarded as "an ultimate one; its object is physical," he said, "rather than metaphysical." And he added these significant words, "From the point of view of the physicist, a theory of matter is a policy rather than a creed; its object is to connect or coordinate apparently diverse phenomena and above all to suggest, stimulate, and direct experiment."

If I tried to sum up in a sentence what seems to me the philosophic implications of the new physics, I should be inclined to paraphrase Sir J. J. Thomson. A mass of experimental evidence in the twentieth century has provided powerful ammunition to those who look upon a scientific theory as a policy and has made untenable at least one theory regarded as a creed. A policy suggests always a guide to action, and of the various interpretations of science that are current today, those seem to me to be the most useful that emphasize the dynamic nature of science. There are philosophers, I realize, who draw a sharp line between knowing and doing and look askance at all philosophizing that seems to tie the search for truth in any way to practical undertakings. But for me, at least, any analysis of the process of testing a statement made in a scientific context leads at once to a series of actions. Therefore, I venture to define science as a series of interconnected concepts and conceptual schemes arising from experiment and observation and fruitful of further experiments and observations. The test of a scientific theory is, I suggest, its fruitfulness—in the words of Sir J. J. Thomson, its ability "to suggest, stimulate, and direct experiment."

The fallacy underlying what some might call the eighteenth- and nineteenth-century misconceptions of the nature of scientific investigations seems to lie in a mistaken analogy. Those who said they were investigating the structure of the universe imagined themselves as the equivalent of the early explorers and map makers. The explorers of the fifteenth and sixteenth centuries had opened up new worlds with the aid of imperfect maps; in their accounts of distant lands, there had been some false and many ambiguous statements. But by the time everyone came to believe the world was round, the maps of distant continents were beginning to assume a fairly consistent pattern. By the seventeenth century, methods of measuring space and time had laid the foundations for an accurate geography. The increased success of empirical procedures in improving the work of artisans was already improving men's accuracy of observation. Therefore, by a series of successive approximations, so to speak, maps and descriptions of distant lands were becoming closer and closer to accurate accounts of reality. Why would not the labors of those who worked in laboratories have the same outcome? No one doubted that there were real rivers, mountains, trees, bays with tides, rainfall, snowfall, glaciers; one could doubt any particular map or description, of course, but given time and patience, it was assumed the truth would be ascertained. By the same token there must be a truth about the nature of heat, light, and matter.

To be sure, the map makers had been observing gross objects like rocks and trees, rivers and mountains, while, as science progressed, the force of gravity and atoms and waves in the ether became the preoccupation of the physicist. Still, tentative ideas played a similar part in both enterprises; working hypotheses as to the nature of a river valley, the source of a lake, or the frontier of a mountain range seemed to be the equivalent of the caloric fluid or the early corpuscular theory of light. The early geographers' methods of identification were essentially those of common sense. Any given set of observations might be in error. Yet even erroneous assumptions might serve, at times, a useful purpose. To have assumed the existence of a lake beyond a certain mountain range might prove fortunate; as a "working hypothesis," even if false, it might lead an explorer to important goals.

Of course, the possibility of error exists in all surveys. Indeed, one can image a situation where even in geography no final certainty is possible. Assume an island surrounded by reefs that make direct access out of the question except with special equipment, and assume an explorer without such equipment. He must content himself for the time being with telescopic observations from several angles; he can thus construct a map but with many uncertainties. For example, are those highly colored areas due to rocks or to vegetation? On his return with adequate equipment, he can land, go to the colored areas and directly determine their composition. If before he returns, the island disappears below the surface of the ocean, that makes no difference as to the validity of his methods. We are all sure that in principle he could have returned and determined the accuracy of his suppositions about the nature of the terrain.

This use of the "in principle" argument, I have already pointed out, was the basis for the nineteenth-century physicist's confidence in his picture of a gas with its rapidly moving particles. Those who still hold today with the idea that the universe has a structure which, like the geography of an island, can be discovered by successive approximations, must cling to the "in principle" argument. Confront them with the phlogiston theory, the caloric fluid, the luminiferous ether—all now obsolete (except for pedagogic purposes)—and they will say,

"Yes, the first maps were imperfect, but in principle it is possible to find out what really is the structure of the universe."

On this basic issue there is far from complete agreement among philosophers of science today. You can, each of you, choose your side and find highly distinguished advocates for the point of view you have selected. However, in view of the revolution in physics, anyone who now asserts that science is an exploration of the universe must be prepared to shoulder a heavy burden of proof. To my mind, the analogy between the map maker and the scientist is false. A scientific theory is not even the first approximation to a map; it is not a creed; it is a policy —an economical and fruitful guide to action by scientific investigators.

But lest my skepticism distort the picture unduly, let me point out how little the new physics has altered some of the older conceptual schemes of physics and chemistry; let me emphasize what an excellent policy the new physics has proved to be in terms of experiments. What disturbs many people are the difficulties that arise if we accept the map-maker analogy. That two conceptual schemes should appear so dissimilar as the wave formulation of the laws governing the transmission of light, on the one hand, and the corpuscular theory of light emission, on the other, distresses those who have looked to the physical sciences for an ever increasing degree of explanation as to how matter is "really constructed." It almost seems as though the modern physicist were like an explorer who, uncertain as to whether the colored areas dimly seen from a distance were rocks or trees, found on landing they were both! But this is a false parallel; it would be far better to say that the physicist seems now to be in the position of an explorer who can never land on the distant island. In short, the whole analogy between a map and a scientific theory is without a basis.

One objection to the point of view I am advocating in these lectures may be considered briefly at this point. It is to the effect that if a scientific theory is not even an approximation to a map of a portion of the universe, the so-called advance of pure science is nothing but a game; from which it would follow, so the objection runs, that the justification of science is to be found only in the application of science to the practical arts. The answer to those who put forward arguments of this type is to remind them of the work of mathematicians, painters, poets, and musical composers. To my mind, the significance of the fabric of scientific theories that have been produced in the last three hundred and fifty years is the same as the significance of the art of the great periods in history, or the significance of the work of the musical composers. For most scientists, I think the justification of their work is to be found in the pure joy of its creativeness; the spirit which moves them is closely akin to the imaginative vision which inspires an artist. To some degree, almost all men today applaud the success of the past in the realm of creative work and do not measure the degree of success by material standards. So too, at some distant time, the advance of science from 1600 to 1950 may be regarded entirely as a triumph of the creative spirit, one manifestation of those vast potentialities of men and women that make us all proud to be members of the human race.

A second objection to the skepticism of those of us who regard all scientific theories as formulations of policy is that our view is only a transitory social phenomenon. One must admit that perhaps the children now in elementary school may in middle life feel that a picture of the universe that seems no picture is quite a satisfactory model. To be sure, it took generations for people to become accustomed to the concept of a force of gravity acting at a distance without any medium to transmit the force. Certainly by the year 2052, relativity and quantum mechanics will occupy a different position in the total science of that day from that assigned to them at present. When these new ideas have been assimilated into the culture of the times, the idea of science as an inquiry into the structure of the universe may once again become firmly established in people's minds.

My bet as to the future, however, is on the other horse. It seems to me more likely that the average citizen will come to think of science in totally different terms from those employed in explaining science to lay audiences fifty years ago. If I am right, in order to assimilate science into the culture of our twentieth-century highly industrialized society, we must regard scientific theories as guides to human action and thus an extension of common sense. At all events, this is the point of view presented in these lectures. Some of the consequences of this outlook for those concerned with science and human conduct will be explored in my next two lectures.

Science and Human Conduct

In the two previous lectures of this series, I have reviewed some aspects of the history of science and technology in this century. In this lecture I propose to explore certain consequences of the revolution in physics in terms of their effect on human conduct. Let me make it quite plain at the outset, however, that I do not intend to focus attention on the science of human conduct (if there be such a science) or on the science of human behavior. This is not to be in any sense a review of recent advances in either psychology or sociology. Not only would such an undertaking be entirely beyond both my capacity and my ambitions, but also it would not serve to direct attention to the problems with which I have dealt in my two previous lectures.

In my first lecture I spoke of the striking social phenomenon of our times—the scientist turned inventor. In my second, I briefly examined the so-called revolution in physics which for many people has cast doubt on the nature of what scientists said they were doing. Fifty or seventy-five years ago the scientist was supposed to be discovering nature's laws; the inventor was taking advantage of these discoveries for practical ends. The old-fashioned inventor has now disappeared; the basic assumptions of those who once popularized science have been challenged. I propose in this lecture and the next to see what, if any, significance the new interpretation of science has for the philosophy of life that guides the daily decisions of thoughtful men and women.

There are two current fallacies about the nature of science; one tends to equate the scientist with a magician, the other confuses him with a mathematician. It is from the second of these popular misconceptions that the notion arises of a sharp dichotomy between the world of science and the realm of values. One's school experience with the theorems of Euclid and the Q.E.D. comes to mind when the words "science" and "truth" are used in the same sentence. According to the general philosophic outlook that I am presenting in these lectures, the truths of the propositions of geometry are inherent in their premises; mathematical or abstract reasoning as such is, in one sense, a vast tautology. But, I hasten to add, this tautology is of enormous value to the scientists because the theorems and operations in this abstract universe of discourse can be related to the world of the experiences of the physical scientist by certain approximations.

The demonstration of mathematical theorems, the

repetition of those experiments whose interpretation has become a matter of common acceptance, the calculations carried out in those areas where the degree of empiricism [1] is low—these activities, we feel, are somehow different from the activities involved in negotiating a treaty between two nations or a contract between two firms or from comforting a friend in sorrow. The first group, it is commonly said, is science; the second, human conduct involving ethics, morals, ideals, and matters of the spirit. But such statements, I believe, are essentially erroneous. The activities I have listed are not science; they are either exercises in logic, or the repetition of activities once significant in the advance of science, or essentially trivial and tiresome mental operations for some practical end, entirely equivalent to making change. Science is a dynamic undertaking directed to lowering the degree of the empiricism involved in solving problems; or, if you prefer, science is a process of fabricating a web of interconnected concepts and conceptual schemes arising from experiments and observations and fruitful of further experiments and observations.

As I have attempted to show in the preceding lectures, science is an activity; many of the results of this activity have become intermeshed with common-sense ideas. Scientific concepts are so much a part of the equipment of men and women in our culture that they are used both consciously and unconsciously in making decisions that we call ethical or moral. The activities of scientists in their laboratories are shot through with value judgments.

[1] For the definition of this phrase, see p. 23.

Such at least is the twofold thesis I am defending now.

The concepts of scientists and their conceptual schemes (such as the atomic theory) can be regarded as serving the same purpose for research workers as do "common-sense ideas" for most people in the routine of living. The intermingling of precepts and concepts involved in the simplest acts of everyday life became a habit with us so early as to defy analysis of their origin. These habitual responses alone enable us to survive. By the time we are able to think at all and handle ourselves in the world, we have a mass of concepts (common-sense ideas) ready at hand. These have come to us in large part as a result of trial and error, in part by experiences that cluster together and which we designate as other persons. In an immediate situation, many of these concepts come into play, as a matter of course, as guides to action. Only philosophers attempt to analyze their origin and question their validity or verifiability. The uniformity of nature is one of these common-sense ideas. Skepticism about such ideas has no place in everyday life. The butcher, the baker, and the candlestick maker may have no valid reasons for believing that the world in which they operate has a uniformity, but they are certain they can slaughter and bake and fabricate by the same rules tomorrow as they have employed all their lives.

The common-sense world is one of partial uniformity only. There are areas of experience where we know that uncertainty is the certainty—the weather is an obvious example and to be contrasted with the regularity of day and night. To operate in a world of partial uniformity, we clearly need rules of experience. And the invention of such rules and of abstract ideas related to such rules has been of the utmost importance in the advance of civilization. Long before the idea of number had emerged, primitive people had evolved the conceptual scheme of a three-dimensional world. There were solid objects which could be seen, felt, and kicked; there were shadows that could be seen but neither felt nor kicked. To tie together all the empirical rules about nature, speculative thinking developed such concepts as those involved in animism and mythology. From the point of view I am here presenting, these ideas must be considered as early prototypes of the far more sophisticated Aristotelian principles and of such scientific theories as the caloric fluid and the luminiferous ether.

As guides to human conduct, common-sense ideas and scientific concepts interpenetrate to such an extent today that no one can say where one begins and the other ends. This is so obvious in regard to all the machinery that surrounds a civilized man that it requires no comment. But it is equally true with respect to habits which are far more primitive than the use of conveniences unknown to the ancient world. Consider our dietary and sanitary habits. Examine your own conduct for a day or two and try to list how many decisions, made at least half consciously, are determined by the findings of scientists in the last one hundred years. There would be many borderline cases which illustrate the point I am trying to make. And the certainty of the decisions would by no means be determined by their relation to modern science.

This last point I should like to dwell on for a moment as it illustrates a matter I believe to be of great importance. Our conduct in regard to eating is tied to deep-seated emotional complexes far more than to scientific theories. Robust individuals have been stimulated to active nausea by being told they had just eaten an article of food outside their dietary code. The Indian guide of a friend of mine was so afflicted when he saw his sophisticated companion start to dine on frogs' legs. This is primitive behavior, you may say, but a long process of education is required to overcome such unconscious responses on the part of even the most highly civilized among us. To what degree long experience with the conceptual schemes of modern science brings about the same deep-seated attachment to these schemes as that expressed by the Indian guide for his beliefs, I do not know. Perhaps a bacteriologist would automatically vomit if convinced that he had swallowed a mass of deadly bacteria; I doubt it. I think he would call for a stomach pump. All this may seem trivial to some of you, but I believe the recognition that there is a distinction between different degrees of attachment to conceptual frameworks is a matter of some importance. Further exploration of this field by psychologists and psychiatrists may yield a rich harvest. Roughly speaking, this is the area in which fall the phenomena investigated by those who study psychosomatic medicine. I shall return to the question of degrees of attachment or conviction as applied to ethical decisions and religious beliefs in my next and concluding lecture.

Tonight I want to confine my attention to decisions affecting human conduct that seem to be fairly evenly balanced, where no deep-seated emotional reactions are involved—rational decisions, we may say. These may range from a determination to buy high-test gasoline rather than a cheaper grade, to the making up of one's mind to sign a petition to outlaw the atomic bomb. Or, if you are in a responsible position in the affairs of this highly industrialized world, you may have to vote yes or no on a proposed loan for the purpose of building a pilot plant to make a new product or a new machine.

There is a fairly common fallacy that if you are dealing with scientific and technical matters, judgment of values rarely, if ever, enters in. Facts speak for themselves in science, we are often told. Anyone who is familiar with the course of scientific research and development knows this is nonsense. What is true is that the area of debate is fairly definitely circumscribed. The proponent of a process for making a new fabric, for example, is unlikely to quote either Plato or Aristotle on behalf of his proposal. Nor is he likely to appeal to the doctrines set forth in the Declaration of Independence or to the decisions of the Supreme Court. But that does not mean that what is proposed is not controversial. It means simply that the number of people qualified to take part in the controversy is highly limited. And this fact is one pregnant with trouble for our free society. Indeed, among the highly significant but dangerous results of the development of modern science is the fact that scientific experts now occupy a peculiarly exalted and isolated position. Of course, this is an age of experts of all types; one of the vital problems of education is to start a trend of mind among our young people that will lead to a better understanding by one group of experts of what other groups of experts are doing. But I cannot take the time tonight to digress into this topic of general education.

The notion that a scientist is a cool, impartial, detached individual is, of course, absurd. The vehemence of conviction, the pride of authorship burn as fiercely among scientists as among any creative workers. Indeed, if they did not, there would be no advance in science. But this emotional attachment to one's own point of view is particularly insidious in science because it is so easy for the proponent of a project to clothe his convictions in technical language. Therefore it is necessary to explore ways and means of balancing the biases of experts whenever their opinions are of prime importance in the making of decisions.

First of all, a healthy skepticism is in order in listening to an expert, particularly an enthusiastic one. The next step is to try to find a person of equal technical competence but with an opposite emotional bias. If such a one is not at hand, some competent individual hitherto unconcerned with whatever project is in question should be asked to undertake the job of being "devil's advocate," as it were. He should be asked to devote himself to preparing the case for a reasoned opposition to what has been proposed. Such procedures for balancing the bias of technical men, particularly scientists turned inventors, have been worked out almost without plan in the successful industries of this nation. But similar methods of operating have not yet been evolved in other areas; they are absent in the United States Government. Yet here they are particularly needed, for, as I pointed out in my first lecture, the government has entered research and development on a very large scale indeed. It is inevitable that in any technological undertaking, conservatism must continually face enthusiasm. In so doing, emotions are aroused and personal fortunes become entangled with technological considerations.

In 1940, those of us who were in Washington as civilians were concerned mostly with the technological conservatism of the men in uniform. I will relate no stories to prove the point. The conflict between the professors and the "brass" is too well known. Most of the versions do less than justice to the military man and give too much credit to the professor. Be that as it may, what I am concerned with is not the technological conservatism of the men in uniform in 1940 but the almost fanatic enthusiasm for research and development of their successors in 1952. It is a phenomenon not unlike that of an old-fashioned religious conversion. The Defense Department, in regard to research, is not unlike the man who sprang onto his horse and rode madly off in all directions.

This is not the time nor place for me to outline in detail my remedy for what many feel to be a bad situation. I will content myself by saying I believe that if the Department of Defense would gradually introduce a quasi-judicial system of review which provided forced opposition to new projects, the taxpayers' money would be more wisely spent. When a question came up to be settled, even if three or four echelons from the top, one or two referees or judges might hear the arguments pro and con. The important point is that there should be arguments *against* the proposal: they should be vigorous but candid; a technical expert should speak on behalf of the taxpayer against each large proposal. Then adequate briefs for the two sides could be prepared (not compromise committee reports). With opposing briefs, arguments, and cross-questioning, many facets of the problem, many prejudices of the witnesses would be brought out into the open. The forced opposition is the important point.

There may be some who feel that my attitude towards science is defeatist, that instead of suggesting how the emotional reactions of scientists should be balanced when they are giving advice about future action, I should demand that scientists act like scientists and eliminate their prejudices. For example, a social scientist in answering affirmatively the question, "Can science save us?" has written as follows:

"Science, as a method, is a form of human behavior. It consists of asking clear, answerable questions in order to direct one's observations, which are made in a calm and unprejudiced manner and which are then reported as accurately as possible and in such a way as to answer the questions that were asked to begin with, after which any pertinent beliefs or assumptions that were held before the observations were made are revised in the light of observations made and answers obtained." All of which is a typical description of what is often called scientific behavior, but I venture to suggest it is not a descrip-

tion of the characteristic way the natural sciences have
advanced; it is rather an account of the use of very limited
working hypotheses not dissimilar to those employed in
everyday life.

To illustrate what I mean by a limited working hypothesis, I shall have to revert for a moment to what I said
in my first lecture about the development of modern science. I suggested that the activity we designate as scientific research is compounded of the empirical procedures
by which man has improved the practical arts ever since
the dawn of civilization, general speculative ideas, and
mathematical or abstract reasoning. Science began to
progress rapidly in the sixteenth and seventeenth centuries when people saw how to relate these three activities.
When employed, the speculative ideas became working
hypotheses on a grand scale; such conceptual schemes
as "the earth is surrounded by a sea of air" could be tested
by experiment only by being connected with actual manipulations by a series of limited working hypotheses.
These are of the type "if I turn this stopcock, then such
and such will happen." Only by a long chain of reasoning is the specific "if, then" proposition, which can be
tested, related to the validity of the working hypothesis
on a grand scale.

To illustrate the relation of limited working hypotheses
to those conceptual schemes which have been essential
for the advance of science, let me analyze a common-sense
inquiry directed to an immediate practical end. Assume
that you are confronted with a locked door and a bunch of
keys; the hypothesis readily comes to mind that one of

these keys will unlock the door. This is a working hypothesis. From it, one can deduce several consequences which can be tested by appropriate action. The most obvious is to try each key in turn in the lock and see if any one will, in fact, unlock the door. This involves a set of experiments which requires a certain degree of order, as care must be taken to test *each* key; also, the keys tested must be in fact those originally under consideration (leaving the keys about for a while and then trying them would necessitate the assumption that no one had made a substitution!). A series of limited working hypotheses thus seems involved somewhat as follows: (1) one of this bunch of keys will unlock the door; (2) this particular key will unlock the door; (3) if this particular key will unlock the door when I insert it in the lock and turn it, then the lock will spring. This last "if, then" proposition can be put to the test and yields a yes or no answer. Depending on the outcome, the next key is tried. Such "if, then" propositions are highly limited working hypotheses of exactly the type used throughout experimental science.

To illustrate what I have in mind, let me give one simple example drawn from the history of science. Pascal in the seventeenth century set out to test the idea that the earth was surrounded by a sea of air which exerted pressure. This he proposed to do by observing the height of a column of mercury in a barometer (to use modern terms). His brother-in-law ascended the Puy de Dôme for this purpose and set up a Torricellian tube (a barometer) on the summit and measured the height of the column of mercury. The experiment confirmed Pascal's prediction, based on the new theory, that the column would be appreciably lower than that observed in a barometer at the base of the mountain. Notice that the grand hypothesis that the earth was surrounded by a sea of air was not and could not be tested directly. The limited working hypothesis that was tested was, essentially, "If I set up this barometer here on the summit and measure the height of the mercury column, it will be less than that observed at the base." The connection between the verification or negation of this limited hypothesis and the broad working hypothesis, namely, that the earth is surrounded by a sea of air, involves many steps and many assumptions.

To illustrate further the long chains of reasoning involved in science, let me return to the trivial case mentioned earlier. Here the restricted working hypothesis was connected with a broader, yet limited, working hypothesis, namely, "one of these keys will unlock the door." The latter is the working hypothesis which a quick glance at the problem indicates is being tested. Yet the connection between the observation, turning the hand, observing the lock, and the working hypothesis that is being tested involves a chain of reasoning as well as common-sense concepts and assumptions. To name but a few of the latter, one need only mention that the words "key," "lock," "turning," and "springing the lock" would be meaningless in many cultures. But even more important are common-sense assumptions such as that the ability of the key to spring a lock will remain unchanged over the period of inquiry, and that each key is the "same" key and the lock is the "same." (The latter assumption might easily be false and the former might be invalidated by a sleight-of-hand performer.) The equivalent of these assumptions and concepts in the case of a scientific experiment is by no means trivial. A vast number of errors have resulted from a failure to examine critically such assumptions. Or, more often, the "errors," as we now call them, came from the fact that assumptions which *had to be made to get ahead* turned out to be only first approximations.

The last point is of significance in view of the attention that is being paid today to the analysis of the methods used in physics. Emphasis is being placed on the need to define, in terms of actual manipulations where possible, the concepts used in physics, such as "length" and "simultaneity." Failure to carry out such rigorous thinking in the past, some authors have implied, has delayed the advance of physics. This may be the case. But if one examines the history of chemistry or biology, it becomes plain that clear-cut operational definitions are never possible in the infancy of science. Rather, early investigators in these fields usually must start with common-sense notions which are bound to be hazy and uncertain. Only by being willing to work with these "fuzzy ideas" and relate them to limited working hypotheses and thus to experiment and observations have the pioneers succeeded.

Take as an example Pasteur's study of fermentation. Here was a word, "fermentation," used to describe a group of everyday processes which over the ages men had learned by empirical procedures to control. No clear-cut definition of "fermentation" was possible in Pasteur's time and one would be difficult today. The change from sugar to alcohol fell within this category and had been shown to be associated with the presence of a micro-organism, yeast. Another change, from starch to sugar, was associated with something found in sprouting barley that could be extracted with warm water. Pasteur put forward as a working hypothesis on a grand scale the concept that all fermentations were the result of the growth of living organisms. To rule out the starch-sugar case, where clearly no living organism was present, he hedged his statement by the phrase, "fermentations properly so called." He then found he could demonstrate the necessary growth of organisms in many changes hitherto classed as fermentations and these became, of course, for him "fermentations properly so called."

Pasteur comes very close to arguing in a circle. This is particularly clear today when we know that both his "fermentations properly so called" and the other similar changes where no organism is present are all brought about by enzymes. Yet one might better call Pasteur's procedure a spiral argumentation, for it certainly was fruitful. It was highly illogical for him to define fermentation so as to exclude the known cases where living organisms were *not* involved and then turn around and point with pride to the instances where fermentation and life were correlative. But his concept as a policy, a guide to action, was successful; indeed, if Pasteur had been more rigorous in his logic, his results might have been less revolutionary.

Unless I am much mistaken, the successful use of hazy

concepts in biology, biochemistry, and, above all, in medicine has deep significance for those concerned with human behavior. John Tyndall, reviewing the application of Pasteur's discoveries to the brewer's art, contrasted "the scientific account of the agencies which come into play in the manufacture of beer" with the hitherto "empirical observations" of the brewers.[2] Pasteur's working hypothesis on a grand scale (namely, that fermentation and life were correlative) was the first major step in lowering the degree of empiricism in the fermentation industries. But we must not forget to what extent pure empiricism over the ages has improved the making of beer and wine, nor the vast amount of empirical knowledge thus accumulated.

Substitute for "fermentation" the words "typhoid fever" or "syphilis" or "pneumonia," and you would be able to trace a somewhat similar path of progress in lowering the degree of empiricism. You would meet the same difficulties in defining the basic concepts (what is a disease in operational terms?), but you would record far less success over the ages in solving the problem by pure empiricism. Indeed, since human lives, not spoiled casks of fermenting juice, are here involved, the errors of pure empiricism loom large in the history of medical sciences. We can laugh at any superstitions of the wine makers of earlier times, but we shudder when we think of the needless deaths due to "bleeding" and similar medical practices now discarded. The trial-and-error procedures of pure empiricism are slow and wasteful, even when they

2 See p. 23.

are well ordered; through them the arts have gradually progressed, but the art of medicine in the process of development undoubtedly shortened the lives of a considerable percentage of those who could afford to consult physicians. Indeed, it is probable that only within this century have medical men and surgeons helped more people than they have injured—one might almost say, cured more persons than they have killed.

The parallel with the social sciences, I suggest, is worth considering. All the sciences concerned with human beings that range from the abstractions of economics through sociology to anthropology and psychology are, in part, efforts to lower the degree of empiricism in certain areas; in part they are efforts to organize and systematize empirical procedures. Whether or not in each of the divisions or subdivisions a Pasteur has yet arisen is not for me to say. But if he has, his contribution has been the introduction of some new broad concepts, some working hypotheses on a grand scale that have been fruitful of further investigations. It would seem important to distinguish, if possible, the advances connected with such broad working hypotheses, which are the essence of a science, and the continued efforts to improve human society by empirical procedures. As to the latter, at least, we may be certain there has been a vast amount of labor expended within recent years.

Many social scientists, I imagine, would not dissent too strongly from the proposition that their whole area of investigation is in a state comparable with that of the biological sciences (including medicine) a hundred or a hundred and fifty years ago. If that be the case, the balance of this century should witness great strides forward; but by the very nature of science (as compared to empiricism), it is impossible to foretell in what precise direction the advance will be made. Which one of the common-sense fuzzy ideas about consciousness, love, or the zest for power will be picked up by a rare genius and be the basis for a vast expansion of fruitful scientific work? Perhaps some of you will say I am being unduly cautious; that already the pioneers have done their work; that in one direction Pavlov has opened new vistas about human behavior, in another, Freud has been at least as successful as was Pasteur.

In attempting to appraise the advance of social sciences as sciences, we are always in the same difficulty as with medicine. It is hard to separate the purely empirical from the scientific; it is impossible to be unconcerned with immediate results and difficult to evaluate practical success or failure. To those who tend to belittle the practical consequences of the work of psychiatrists, psychologists, and sociologists, I offer for consideration the interesting case of Dr. Thomas Beddoes of Bristol, England. An eminent physician of the early nineteenth century, abreast of the advances in science, he founded a pneumatic institute for the treatment of disease by means of the new gases discovered not long before. James Watt designed effective machinery for administering the gases to the patients, and a brilliant youth by the name of Humphrey Davy received his start in science by serving as the chemist. It is fortunate no one was killed; it is certain no one was cured. But Dr. Beddoes was no charlatan. In a charitable mood one may even claim he was a chemotherapist a hundred and fifty years ahead of his time and employing the wrong chemicals!

Neither medicine nor the medical sciences were advanced in Dr. Beddoes' Pneumatic Institute. But the same spirit that prompted him has been at work in countless other members of his profession; gradually at first, and with amazing speed in this century, the medical sciences as sciences have advanced. In retrospect we do not count the honest follies of men like Dr. Beddoes nor the innumerable charlatans who follow in such men's wake. So, too, in the whole field of the social sciences; it seems to me probable that a hundred years hence the historians will be able to separate out the science from the empiricism and both from the charlatanism of the 1950's. We are too much immersed in the pioneer stage to be able to make this appraisal ourselves. But surely those who demand progress, with capital letters, in the social sciences and believe it can be achieved by planned attack and exhortation might well profit by reading the history of medicine in the nineteenth century.

If there be any lessons to be drawn from history, they are surely that while advances in science are never divorced from empirical processes, they arise from the most unexpected quarters. Success in lowering the degree of empiricism comes suddenly from one knows not where. Not long after Dr. Beddoes was making his frontal attack on disease by means of the new chemistry, a French physicist, Baron Charles Cagniard de la Tour, demonstrated that yeast globules essential for beermaking were organized bodies belonging to the vegetable kingdom. Who could have guessed that the French physicist rather than the English doctor was starting down the track that was to lead to the control of infectious diseases? The hits in science are usually made with a crooked ball.

The implication of what I have just been saying for those who wish to assist the social sciences is obvious: support the uncommitted investigator who has ideas, irrelevant as these ideas may seem to practical problems. The practical arts, including the art of human relations, are bound to progress, even if slowly, by trial-and-error methods; society is always ready to assist such undertakings. The successes here are not to be despised, even if they are empirical; just as today in metallurgy, as I pointed out in my first lecture, there is a vast amount of empiricism mixed with some science, so, too, the same situation exists in many of the social sciences. In this century we have refined the process of trial-and-error experimentation; we have learned wisdom about empirical procedures. The record of industry demonstrates this beyond question, as far as the natural sciences are concerned. A candid review of what has been accomplished in pedagogy, in handling some types of abnormal psychology, in a few restricted areas of economics, perhaps in certain kinds of human relations, would show progress and would demonstrate that we can solve certain types of problems involving human beings better than our ancestors.

The demand for practitioners in these fields continues

high; but one need not be a cynic to remember that the services of physicians were eagerly sought by the sick even when the members of this profession were on the whole doing more harm than good. There is no need for one to be a Pollyanna optimist to remember that if by edict the practice of medicine had been stopped throughout the Western world, mankind never would have learned to control infectious diseases. Errors in practice as well as in theory appear to be the inescapable price we pay for progress in learning to solve problems.

Now, a final word as to science and human conduct. Literally every step we take in life is determined by a series of interlocking concepts and conceptual schemes. Every goal we formulate for our actions, every decision we make, be it trivial or momentous, involves assumptions about the universe and about human beings. To my mind, any attempt to draw a sharp line between common-sense ideas and scientific concepts is not only impossible but unwise. Belief in the whole apparatus of a three-dimensional world and in the existence of other people is a policy essential for an individual's survival; for a physicist or chemist in his laboratory, a new working hypothesis is a policy guiding his conduct as an experimenter. Where is one to draw the line? The common-sense ideas of our ancestors before the dawn of modern science were the foundation of all their value judgments. If scientific concepts are now part of our common-sense assumptions, and who can doubt they are, then to this degree, at least, the consequences of the actions of previous scientists now affect our value judgments. This much connection between science and human conduct seems to me quite certain.

In his laboratory, every scientist is forever deciding that this is a better way to proceed than that. Every experiment he plans was, in its inception, cradled by judgments of what would be worth while, what would warrant the effort, including an over-all value judgment that the investigator should stay in his laboratory rather than go fishing.

At this point some of you may be inclined to say with impatience, if not with heat, "For a whole hour the main guide to human conduct has been ignored! Not a word about ethics, not a mention of morals, no reference to religion." To which I would reply that an analysis of the relation of values to science and of both to relatively trivial examples of human decisions appears to me to be a necessary prelude to a consideration of the Big Questions of the nature and destiny of man and the problem of good and evil. To what extent modern science has anything to say to the individual who ponders on the meaning of life, on definitions of moral standards, and on the whole realm of spiritual values depends on certain basic philosophic presuppositions. These presuppositions, in turn, reflect one's attitude toward science.

Reverting to my previous lecture, I will remind you that a scientific concept can be regarded either as a policy or as a creed. If the latter, then this creed is equivalent to a map of the material universe (even if only a first approximation) and must be congruous with an account of human beings and their destiny. A consistent, unitary World Hypothesis with appropriate subcategories for man, for life, for matter, for energy, has been the goal of theologians and philosophers for centuries. In the eighteenth and nineteenth centuries, scientists joined hands with such endeavors. Before the revolution in physics, this looked like a simpler undertaking than it has in fact turned out to be. It is interesting that among those who formulated a scientific creed in the opening years of this century there were both optimists and pessimists. The same assumptions (or very nearly the same assumptions) could lead to quite different moods. As to the optimists I shall have something to say in my next lecture. This lecture I conclude by quoting what Bertrand Russell wrote in his *A Free Man's Worship* fifty years ago. Speaking of "the world which science presents for our belief," he wrote, "That man is the product of causes which had no prevision of the end they were achieving; that his origin, his growth, his hopes and fears, his loves and his beliefs, are but the outcome of accidental collocations of atoms; that no fire, no heroism, no intensity of thought and feeling, can preserve an individual life beyond the grave; that all the labors of the ages, all the devotion, all the inspiration, all the noonday brightness of human genius, are destined to extinction in the vast death of the solar system, and that the whole temple of Man's achievement must inevitably be buried beneath the debris of a universe in ruins—all these things, if not quite beyond dispute, are, yet so nearly certain, that no philosophy which rejects them can hope to stand. Only within the scaffolding of these truths, only on the firm foundation of unyielding despair, can the soul's habitation henceforth be safely built." [*]

In using this quotation, I think it only fair to say that I doubt if the distinguished philosopher would express these views today in the same language. But the difficulty of assuming that science is a creed or part of a creed, a map of the universe, however imperfect, is illustrated by this quotation. The modern cosmology is based on experimental results unimagined fifty years ago and this cosmology is subject to a somewhat different interpretation from that of Russell in 1903. Whether or not any of these interpretations bear on the problem of good and evil is a question I shall consider in my concluding lecture.

[*] First published in *Independent Review*, December, 1903; included in *Mysticism and Logic and Other Essays* (Longmans, Green, and Co., London and New York, 1918); separately published as *A Free Man's Worship* (Mosher, Portland, Maine, 1923).

Science and Spiritual Values

IN MY LAST LECTURE I explored the false antithesis between science and value judgments. Let me continue this exploration by examining the impact of science on one type of conduct that is associated with a moral judgment shared in common by many different cultural groups. A recurring phenomenon in history is the attempt of individuals to mitigate the physical suffering of others. In the Judaic-Christian tradition such attempts have been given a high status; they have been portrayed as examples of a conduct to be emulated. So much so that out of a hundred people picked at random here in New York, I would wager at least ninety would assert that helping the sick and suffering was "good" and that indifference or cruelty was "bad." Furthermore, a large majority would have demonstrated by their actions their adherence to this value judgment. The reasons for the judgment would

cover a wide range, but whether expressed in dogmatic
religious terms or related only to broad philosophic ideas,
almost all of these come within the scope of what I am
going to call "the realm of spiritual values." In one way
or another it is implied or explicitly stated that an unselfish act is a good act; that quite apart from the social
consequences to the individual performing the act, lend-
ing a hand to a sufferer is something a person ought to
do.

Whatever may be the basis for our belief in the impera-
tive, "Help the suffering," this precept can be an effective
guide for conduct only insofar as one has power to alleviate such suffering. It need hardly be pointed out that
the advance of the medical sciences has made possible
the mitigation of many types of human misery to a degree
undreamt of a few centuries ago. The present status of
medicine and public health is the result of the efforts of
thousands of scientists over the last three hundred years.
Admittedly, many of these men were not motivated in
the least by their concern with suffering humanity. Indeed, some were totally unaware of the fact that their
work would throw light on the problems of the physician.
On the other hand, in the last hundred years a great many
investigators have been prompted by their desire to improve the ancient art of healing; not only physicians but
chemists and biologists as well.

A conscious effort on the part of many investigators
to control disease, to prolong life, and to alleviate pain
has yielded results of a most dramatic nature. I should
like to point out that the conduct of almost every indi-

vidual who participated in this advance of science and
progress in the art of healing was determined by a set
of value judgments. These judgments were closely connected with the exhortation, "One ought to help the suffering." The conduct of doctors, we all know, is regu-
lated by a set of ethical principles which in themselves
are based on value judgments. What I am here emphasizing is the degree to which a judgment of value has determined the investigation of scientists or those seeking
by empirical means to improve an art. Once again I make
the point that those who say that science and value judgments are in separate compartments have failed to examine the nature of scientific undertakings and the motivation of many scientists.

Considering how much is now published about technical achievements in the way of atomic bombs, poison gas,
even the possibility of bacteriological and radiological
warfare, it is well to stop a moment and recognize what
an army of men and women is now employed in helping
sufferers by means of tools provided by modern science.
This is something quite different from providing addi-
tional creature comforts, raising the standard of living,
increasing the pleasures of either the mind or the flesh.
Much of what our modern industrial civilization pro-
duces for the consumer can be branded as materialistic—
the invention of the devil, some ascetic Christian funda-
mentalists would say. But strengthening the hand of the
Good Samaritan is an entirely different matter. This consequence of science needs to be underlined. If loving
your neighbor as yourself is the epitome of a religious

outlook, it can only have meaning as a policy to the extent that one is able to help the neighbor when he or she is in pain or trouble.

As to relieving physical pain, there can be no doubt of the effectiveness of the advance of science. Whether a hundred years from now a similar statement will be possible about emotional and mental suffering, no one can say. The hope that this may be the case is surely one of the factors spurring on the efforts of those who study the behavior of human beings. Once again a value judgment is seen at work.

The whole idea that the practical arts can be improved by other than empirical procedures is relatively new, as I pointed out in my first lecture. As a firm conviction on the part of a number of influential citizens, this idea is a product of the seventeenth century. That the arts thus improved included the healing arts was inherent in the dreams of the proponents of the new experimental philosophy of that time; making these dreams come true has taken much longer than many of them imagined. On the other hand, all sorts of powers have been made available for transforming nature, for transportation, and for communication that could not have been imagined three hundred years ago. From the Renaissance on, there was an increasing stream of opinion in Christian countries to the effect that some of the sufferings of the human race could be relieved by human action. Utopias were depicted where not only did milk and honey flow, but disease was cured, pain removed. That the alleviation of physical distress would be not only desirable but also in the spirit of the Christian religion, only a few doubted. Those who did would be likely to turn to the Book of Job.

The problem of evil as set forth in the Book of Job is not the problem of evil conduct on the part of humans but the problem of why good men suffer grievous calamities. The problem is recurring; what one of us has not felt its bruising impact within the year? Of the answers given by Job's comforters, none suggested that some evils of the flesh could be overcome by human action. Yet this in essence seem to me the eighteenth century's rationalistic answer to Job's laments. It was an answer that ever since has been echoed by ardent supporters of the work of scientists. Forty years ago it was widely accepted by what are now called "liberal" Christians; in the last twenty years, doubts as to its validity have been expressed by certain Protestant leaders as well as Catholics. The liberal tradition, it is constantly asserted today, has been forced "by the wry advance of world events to adjust its large principles to the hard reality of things as they are." Of the world events, Hitler, Stalin, and the explosion of the atomic bomb are usually cited as examples.

If I read the Book of Job correctly, its lesson is a denial of the assumption that the universe is explicable in human terms; it is a corrective to the presumption of human beings in applying their standards of value to the cosmos. The Lord rebukes Job's three comforters for their attempt to persuade the sufferer that he must have sinned by arguing that otherwise he would not have been afflicted. The universe is not constructed along the lines of an automatic machine distributing rewards and punishments—at least not in this world of mortals. As to a future life, the Book of Job reflects the Judaic as contrasted to the Christian position; the New Testament answer to the problem of evil is largely absent in the Old Testament. And as to the exact meaning of that answer, Christians have been debating for nearly two thousand years.

Salvation by good works as opposed to salvation by faith, I shall not discuss. Rather I wish to stay within the setting of the Book of Job. The writer presents two answers, it seems to me, to the question of why men and women of the purest character may suffer the most hideous afflictions. The first is essentially that the universe is inexplicable. With almost a stoic resignation, Job accepts this fact and ceases to lament. This is the philosophic answer; the other is the spiritual one; it may be expressed in Job's own words. After the Lord had answered him out of the whirlwind, Job said, "I have heard of thee by the hearing of the ear; but now mine eye seeth thee. Wherefore I abhor myself, and repent in dust and ashes."

Taken literally, this passage means something very specific in theological terms to an orthodox Jew or fundamentalist Christian. Taken symbolically, it has deep spiritual meaning for those who interpret broadly the Judaic-Christian literature. I shall so regard it. Indeed, to those who ask, "What do you mean by the term 'spiritual values'?" I would reply by reference to this episode in the Book of Job.

To explain further what I have in mind, let me give one example of an evaluation that seems to me significant. People have undergone a spiritual enrichment as a conse-

quence of their sufferings, I would say, if they have become less rebellious in their attitude towards the universe,
less frightened of the future, more sympathetic towards
other people; on the other hand, those who have become
more embittered, more apprehensive, more hostile have
suffered a spiritual deterioration. Such changes are only
partially indicated by the verbal formulations of the individual in question; the state of a person's spirit is indicated far more by actions than by formal statements of a
philosophy of life. Judgments of the type I have just mentioned seem to me to have meaning and to be concerned
with a value we may well call spiritual.

The twofold answer of the Book of Job stands in
sharp contradiction to the belligerent optimism of a
typical nineteenth-century materialist. For such a person
there was only one explanation of Job's afflictions—ignorance. Disease could be conquered if scientists kept at work
and people were sensible enough to follow their advice;
so, many an intelligent person maintained as early as the
1800's. And as a bit of prophecy, I submit, fewer statements by optimists have ever been more right. This needs
to be emphasized in these days when prophets of gloom
are so readily listened to on all sides. We have been
triumphantly successful in our efforts to right the scales
of apparent injustice in this vale of tears, at least as regards
the ills of the flesh; and it was this type of affliction—
Satan's touching "his bone and his flesh"—which finally
moved Job to question God's justice.

But it is one thing to make great progress in curing or
preventing disease and another to say that *all* the afflic-

tions of man can be overcome by human intelligence. Yet this almost became the creed of those who, throughout the nineteenth century and well into this, proclaimed the coming salvation of man on this earth by the good works known as science! This outlook on the world has become embodied—one might almost say enshrined—in the set of doctrines known as dialectical materialism. One version of these doctrines is the official philosophy of the Kremlin and all those who obey its injunctions and slavishly follow its moods. Another version is, I believe, the accepted philosophy of the Communists of Yugoslavia; in less belligerent and doctrinaire form, the Russian version is accepted by some non-Communist Marxists in English-speaking countries. But in all its forms, it breathes that spirit of the mid-nineteenth century which was carrying forward the rationalistic optimism of the eighteenth.

To the doctrinaire dialectical materialist, the Book of Job is worse than nonsense—it is an opiate of the people. His answer to the problem of all evil, to calamities of all sorts, is essentially as follows: Through science all evils may be overcome. By "science" he means science based on the doctrine of dialectical materialism, the laws that govern not only inanimate nature but the development of society as well. Of these laws, the recognition of the triad—thesis, antithesis, synthesis—as illustrated by the equation, heat plus ice equals water, is usually given prominence in popular expositions.

I do not propose to discuss the grim political consequences of accepting the Soviet interpretation of dialectical materialism. Philosophically the whole doctrine

seems to me utter nonsense. It presents in the most dogmatic and extravagant form the optimism of those scientists who are interested in translating their discoveries
into practical effects. It is a creed suited in a crude way
to the scientist turned inventor, for it glorifies his role;
more than that, it denies that the scientist ever was anything more than an inventor or ever could be. Indeed,
this point of view has been widely publicized by some
non-Marxists who to my mind have unwittingly swallowed a bit of the Communist bait!

I have purposely placed before you a false dichotomy—
the Book of Job taken literally or dialectical materialism.
I have already suggested, I hope, my own predilection;
I would not repudiate the nineteenth-century optimism
about the continued improvement, with the aid of science, of all the practical arts (including the art of human
relations). I would not, however, subscribe to any "in
principle" argument about what science can accomplish.
I would be certain that for the next century, under the
best conditions, the areas of uncertainty and empiricism [1]
would remain enormous. As to the Book of Job, I would
subscribe to the answer that the universe is essentially
inexplicable and I would interpret Job's vision symbolically, using this as one entrance to the whole area of inquiry that can be designated as the universe of spiritual
values.

Before proceeding further with an exposition of my
own ideas about the relation of the realm of spiritual

[1] The philosophically minded reader is reminded that I am using the
word "empiricism" as defined on p. 23; see also p. 26.

values to the universes of inquiry wherein, as practical men and scientists, human beings daily operate, let me remind you that many scientists interpret modern physics in a different light. To them, not only does the universe have a structure of which modern physical theory provides at least an approximate picture (though a very difficult one to explain, they must admit), but the history of this universe is also of significance. Here there is a cleavage among those who take seriously the map-maker analogy of my previous lectures. Some would adhere to a naturalistic evolutionary philosophy not too unlike that of certain nineteenth-century materialists. Others see in the new physics, and above all in the most recent cosmology, evidence for some form of theism quite compatible with the Judaic-Christian tradition.

I quote two recent authors to illustrate the latter trend in modern thought. Sir Edmund Whittaker in his *Space and Spirit*, written in 1946, expresses the opinion that "the achievement of mathematical physics is precisely this, that it has constructed a scheme of the universe which is trustworthy (that is, predictions based on it are always verified by experience), and which can be carried backward . . . to a time before the emergence of any sentient creature." After stating that "the line of descent of the modern physicist is to be traced not from the humanists of the Renaissance, but from the schoolmen of the twelfth and thirteenth centuries," he concludes his review of the theories of the universe and the arguments for the existence of God as follows:

"It cannot be denied, however, that natural theology

is not an altogether straightforward matter to the inquirer who has been trained in the ways of modern science. The aim of the present work has been to indicate—for the consideration of theologians who are not men of science—what the obstacles are, and to show—for the consideration of the scientific inquirer—that they are less formidable than has sometimes been supposed, and moreover, that the deeper understanding of the nature of the material universe . . . has opened up new prospects and possibilities to the advocate of belief in God." [2]

Pascual Jordan in his *Physics of the Twentieth Century*, published in 1944, gives a clear exposition of those new ideas to which I referred briefly in my second lecture. He does not seek to escape the difficulties inherent in the altered picture; for example, he writes, "From a really modern standpoint the older idea of the atom must be regarded as just as much disproved as confirmed, since the corpuscular concept considers only one side of the picture, neglecting the other complementary side. If the quantum theory strips the atom of its clear tangible qualities and leaves only a framework of mathematical formulae for its characterization, our theory of knowledge attitude is confirmed again—physical research aims not to disclose a 'real existence' of things from 'behind' the appearance world, but rather to develop thought systems for the control of the appearance world." In spite of this and similar expressions which seem to place Jordan on the side of those who regard scientific theories as policies

[2] *Space and Spirit* (Chicago: Henry Regnery Co., copyright 1948), pp. 128–29. Reprinted with permission of the publishers.

rather than creeds, his account of the modern ideas of cosmology is as definite as that of a geographer about a thoroughly explored island, for he writes: "It might well have been expected that the great sun were a much older inhabitant of the universe than the small earth expelled from it; but as we see, that is not the cast at all. [He is referring to the data from radioactivity as to the age of the earth.] No less remarkable are the results of age determinations on meteors which likewise become possible through radioactivity investigations. . . . If we summarize our knowledge up to the present, we must say that we have found no body the age of which was shown to be higher than ten billion years. . . . Let us look back into the past; the world diameter, growing with the velocity of light, was formerly smaller than it is now; if we mentally pursue the development of the universe farther and farther back, we come to a point where everything is at an end, or rather, everything is at the beginning . . . ten billion years ago . . . the initially small universe arose from an original explosion." He concludes his book as follows:

"It is remarkable that modern natural research gives rise to knowledge and ideas which drive our feelings in such different directions from those of natural research from the times of Lamettrie to Haeckel. It is doubtless very justifiable for the author of a modern book on the mathematical theories of relativity and cosmology to pronounce at the conclusion that our scientific research on the future and past of the universe need not be influenced by human desires and hopes or by theological theories of

creation. It is also characteristic that the state of development of our science suddenly makes such warnings necessary again.

"But when we pay just recognition to this warning,
when we don't allow any motivation for our scientific research other than the inexorable striving after the knowledge of truth, who would hinder us afterwards from once
dreaming about the results achieved?

"And certainly this picture of the universe as exploding
fireworks which went off ten billion years ago invites us
to consider the remarkable question of Miguel de Una-
muno, whether the whole world—and we with it—be not
possibly only a dream of God; whether prayer and ritual
perhaps be nothing but attempts to make HIM more
drowsy, so that HE does not awaken and stop our dreaming." [3]

I have referred to these two writers in order to do justice
to one significant trend in the recent interpretations of
the relation of modern science to the predicament of
modern man. Time does not permit me to review the neo-
Thomistic approach to the same subject; nor consider to
what extent a faith in the ability of modern science to give
a clear description of the structure and history of the
universe will conflict with faith in the evidence presented
in the New Testament, which, if taken literally, requires
belief in lapses in the validity of the laws of the conservation of mass and energy. I have seen no attempt by funda-

[3] Pascual Jordan, *Physics of the Twentieth Century* (New York: Philosophical Library, Inc., 1944). Reprinted with permission of the publishers.

mentalists, who might welcome the new cosmological theories as evidence for a creation and a creator, to handle the problem of the empty tomb in terms of any scientific conceptual scheme.

My own inclinations lie in a totally different direction. Scientific theories are guides to the action of scientists which gradually become part of our common-sense ideas about the material universe. They have little or no bearing on the age-old problem of good and evil. I would attach meaning to Job's vision, but a symbolic meaning. Inquiries into the nature of this meaning would be inquiries about what I have called spiritual values.

The dialectical materialists and also some agnostics would question whether the universe of inquiry I have just postulated is more than a name for a mythology. They would relate all ethical behavior to the welfare of society or to an individual's adaptation to human relationships. Some sort of materialistic World Hypothesis would provide a unifying principle; there would be no place for any theistic interpretation. Almost certainly these people would maintain that advances in the social and biological sciences could eventually result in the final substitution of value judgments based on science for those now accepted as part of our Judaic-Christian tradition, that it would be possible some day for psychiatry, social psychology, biology, and anthropology to occupy this whole area of inquiry. Yet they would hardly challenge the statement that a vast number of value judgments today contain elements that have no connection with science. The question then appears to come down to this: Can those value judgments that do not now involve scientific concepts be replaced in principle by those that have originated in scientific investigations?

I have referred more than once in these lectures to this "in principle" argument and expressed my suspicion of it. To me, its use indicates an attempt by someone who is constructing a new hypothesis to overreach himself. I doubt if the employment of this type of argument has advanced the physical sciences, though it has often inflated the ego of some scientists. I doubt its applicability to the wider topic that I am attempting to explore; there is nothing to be gained by asserting that in principle all our common-sense ideas about the universe and human behavior, all our ethical principles, and our moral convictions could be replaced by "concepts growing out of experiment and observation." Even in the restricted area of the physical sciences there are huge spots where empiricism alone is the guide for the conduct of scientists as scientists. One can argue that for the sake of his morale a scientific investigator must believe that in principle all these spots can be eliminated. Possibly this may be true, but I doubt it. All that an ardent scientist has to believe is that the lowering of the degree of empiricism can go on indefinitely, not infinitely; as a cautious investigator he should be wary of unnecessary and unwise extrapolations.

As to the unifying, materialistic World Hypothesis, my doubt stems from its manifest inadequacy. As a conceptual scheme attempting to account for everything in the whole universe, it seems to me unsatisfactory because it is incomplete. It fails to provide for the altruistic and idealistic side of human nature. It fails to accommodate what I regard as highly significant facts, not facts of science but facts of human history. These are the unselfish ways in which human beings often act with compassion, love, friendliness, self-sacrifice, the desire to mitigate human suffering. In short, it is the problem of "good," not "evil," that requires some other formulation of human personality than that provided by the usual naturalistic moralist. On the other hand, the formulations that attempt to include spiritual values, modern physics, biology, and cosmology within one total consistent scheme attempt, to my mind, far too much. Whether the unifying principle can be a dualism of matter and spirit, mechanism, formism, or some form of idealism, the whole attempt seems to me to be in the wrong direction. My preference would be for more adequate exploration of special limited areas of experience; one of these would include those experiences which can be ordered in terms of a system of spiritual values.

Each of these restricted areas of exploration I venture to designate a universe of inquiry. I do so only to underline my objection to those who insist on using the "in principle" argument to relate concepts in one set of inquiries to those used in another. Such insistence is, of course, almost second nature for those who regard a scientific theory as a creed or a map of at least a portion of the universe. But for those who regard scientific concepts and conceptual schemes as policies and guides for action, the need for an "in principle" consistency between inquiries in different areas disappears. If two policies in two areas (universes of inquiry, to use my phrase) can actually be brought into conflict as guides to action, then an observational or experimental test between them becomes possible. The conflict generates, so to speak, a series of limited working hypotheses, a chain of reasoning that finally eventuates in a hypothesis so restricted that a fairly clean-cut yes or no answer can be obtained. But if attempts to bring the two policies into conflict fail, as in the case of the corpuscular and wave theories of light, then one may say that the two theories are so dissimilar as to constitute incompatible universes of inquiry. In the case of physics, the possibility of this dissimilarity was denied for years by those who clung to the "in principle" type of argumentation.

How many universes of inquiry can be conveniently recognized today I would not care to state. For practical purposes two or more may be telescoped and treated as one by means of suitable postulates and sets of rules. In a sense, a unitary theory can be constructed to handle the dissimilarities of two universes of inquiry. This is what has occurred in modern physics, according to my reading of recent scientific history. When the highly limited working hypotheses in each area can be formulated quantitatively, then, by the use of mathematical reasoning, the unitary theory can be so stated as to be a very useful policy—so useful, in fact, that if its origins are not carefully traced, one can easily be deceived into thinking it represents a consistent map of one section of the universe.

Within the general field of the natural sciences, I suggest that those inquiries that involve the assumption of the uniformity of nature over long periods of time constitute a special universe of inquiry (or perhaps a group of such universes). To what degree the concepts used in paleontology, for example, must be in principle entirely consistent or compatible with those employed in biochemistry is for me an open question. Such questions arise, for example, whenever cosmologists, biologists, and chemists discuss the origin of life. Many of the so-called theories of the origin of life are not scientific theories at all in the sense of being guides to action. They are merely speculative ideas which no one now knows how to connect with new experiments or observations. On this point, by the way, the general public is apt to be much confused. People fail to distinguish between a new theory about the origin of life (or the origin of granite or of petroleum), which is merely one more speculative idea, and a theory from which flow new consequences that can be tested. Speculation in the field of cosmogony is not to be disparaged, but the wide publicity given to each new flight of fancy tends to confuse the general public and encourage credulity.

The point of view I have presented regards scientific theories as restricted policies, not parts of a unified cosmic creed. I am well aware that it can be attacked in the name of man as a rational being. It can be labeled defeatist, obscurantist,[4] or just a lazy man's way out of embarrassing

[4] I doubt if believers in astrology, bizarre interpretations of astronomy, or modern necromancy will find any comfort in these lectures. A basically skeptical outlook, even if it denies the ability of science to provide a map of the structure of the universe, can hardly provide a platform for the superstitious. The extension of common-sense ideas by domesticated scientific concepts provides the framework of the modern world. The burden of proof is heavy on one who claims to have found a new effect contradicting accumulated practical experience.

difficulties. The adherents of a religious creed which sets
forth in detail the origin, nature, and destiny of man are
almost sure to repudiate any view of the universe that is
as provisional and fragmentary as the one I am suggesting.
Materialistic atheists, interestingly enough, react in much
the same fashion. Indeed, as witnesses for my defense I
might call representative proponents of various unitary
systems, including systems expressed in theological terms,
and by cross-questioning show the diversity of their arguments. There would be no agreement among them, that
much is clear. Another witness might be, of course, a
modern physicist confronted with the ghost of his professional grandfather. On the consequences of such a con-
frontation I need not elaborate, for I have already pointed
out that as regards particles and waves, the present picture
would be regarded by the nineteenth-century physicists as
the juxtaposition of two theories so dissimilar as to be in
principle incompatible.

A view of the universe that rejects the necessity for a
unified World Hypothesis consistent in principle throughout is not defeatist as regards the advance of science. For
if one regards scientific theories as guides to investigations, each theory is continuously open to testing by experiment and observation. Such a view leads to suspicion
of all assumptions carried over from one area of investigation to another. It represents a skeptical approach to
all arguments divorced from actual observation or experimentation. It places the burden of proof on those who
claim that *all* of a given set of concepts are, in practice

as well as in principle, in the same universe of inquiry. There is nothing in such an outlook to discourage attempts to bring different scientific theories into close relation. On the contrary, since the compatibility of two theories can only be determined by the consequences of an apparent conflict and never can be assumed, the emphasis is on observation and experiment rather than on speculative thinking or abstract reasoning.

"The man of action has to believe, the inquirer has to doubt; the scientific investigator is both." This statement of Charles S. Pierce will serve to direct attention to the two fold purpose that many of our general ideas must fulfill. At least some of the concepts and conceptual schemes with which we as scientific investigators work must have a provisional status. They are working hypotheses on a grand scale, to use the terminology of a previous lecture. On the other hand, even in scientific investigations, some of the ideas that originated in the early advance of science must be regarded as having a more durable status. They must, that is, if progress is to be made. If a scientist attempted, every time he entered his laboratory, to retrace the steps in the development of the scientific theories he takes for granted, he would go mad.

When the scientist steps out of his laboratory and takes part in activities other than research, as a man of action he has to believe. The philosopher, whose profession it is to doubt, is under the same compulsion. All of us as sane individuals accept without a flicker of doubt a mass of concepts whose origin is obscure because they have been part of each of us as long as we can remember. As children, at least, we never doubted the reality of a three-dimensional world or the existence of other people. In other words, our degree of attachment to a certain set of ideas is so high as to constitute a belief. The reality of other people, of a solid world with a past and future, and of the partial uniformity of nature are thus matters of common-sense faith. Our degree of conviction as to the correctness of this faith is so great that I do not think anyone can question it in the sense that one questions the existence of a neutrino or even the germ theory of disease. To entertain the solipsist doctrine is not possible in the sense that it is possible for a beginner to consider the pros and cons of the caloric theory of heat.

Scientists have a degree of attachment to some scientific theories almost as great as that which all of us have for the concepts of a real world of rocks and trees and people. There is obviously no clear-cut line. Faith in the validity of the principles of physics and chemistry over billions of years and in the reality of a cosmic history is essential for an astronomer, a geologist, or a paleontologist. This is completely unnecessary and often lacking in a microbiologist or a nuclear physicist, to choose only two examples of scientists who are investigating immediate occurrences. An organic chemist's belief in the reality of atoms arranged in three-dimensional patterns in a molecule is usually almost as great as his belief in the existence of other people. But his predecessors of the nineteenth century held the same views to be highly provisional, it may be noted. And lest anyone be tempted to generalize from this instance and say that the history of all science has been from provisional belief to faith, I would remind you of the discarded theories of phlogiston, the caloric fluid, the luminiferous ether, and the idea that the electron could be exactly located within a molecule.

As a man of action, each of us must not only manipulate a world of inanimate nature full of all sorts of plants and animals (including pathogenic bacteria), but also accommodate ourselves to other people. We must have not only common-sense concepts about a real world, but also some general principles about those entities we believe to be other personalities. We must deal as best we can with what William James has called "the whole paradoxical physico-moral-spiritual Fatness." Only as an inquirer, philosophical or scientific, can a man "single out some skinny fragment" of this Fatness.

For many people in the Western world the concepts that are particularly relevant to human intercourse are religious doctrines. For some, these are provisional beliefs; for others, ideas to which the degree of attachment is extremely high. This is particularly true for those who have grown up in an orthodox form of Christianity or have undergone a conversion of the type described by William James in his *Varieties of Religious Experience.* The parallel with the common-sense belief that other people exist and with the geologists' belief in a geologic past can hardly be denied. Therefore, I am not inclined to quarrel with those who say that a faith in the reality of the God of Calvin, or the God of Catholicism, or the Jehovah of Orthodox Judaism is the same sort of faith as faith in a real external world. But I would question the correctness of considering a belief in God which carries no consequences for the believer as parallel to a belief in the reality of other people which clearly carries some meaning for everyone, except perhaps the sole inhabitant of a desert isle.

Those people who have a high degree of attachment to the beliefs that are orthodox within a certain religion may well be said to have a firm conviction that their theology is not only right but also real. Others may have different degrees of faith in regard to various parts of the total doctrine. But in general, all those who adhere even loosely to a formal religious creed will wish to substitute the word "religious" for "spiritual" wherever I have used the term in this lecture. They would probably not agree that there is any separate universe of inquiry embracing religious values, for their theology would involve a unitary World Hypothesis; but as to the reality of what I have called the realm of spiritual values, they would have no doubt.

My concluding remarks will be addressed not to those whose theology is so certain as to be comparable with a belief in the reality of an external world. Nor will they be addressed to those whose picture of the universe leaves no room for spiritual values. Neither the Christian who interprets the Bible literally rather than symbolically nor the materialist will find any sense in what follows. But for the others I should like to suggest that in regard to many phenomena, we require, as men of action, at least provisional beliefs. These phenomena are open to scientific investigation, but until the degree of empiricism has been greatly lowered, we must operate with rules of conduct that are *not* based on science. This being so, I doubt if we can escape some attempt to put these rules into a conceptual scheme, however hazy. The evidence for the scheme is not affected one way or another by findings of the scientist, whether he be a physical scientist or social scientist. The evidence is based on personal experience and its prolongation by history. It is in the category of naive common-sense assumptions about a world of objects and persons. In the background of most people's thoughts there appears to be a World Hypothesis to portions of which, at least, they have a high degree of attachment. Just as I doubt our ability to think ourselves into the state of solipsism, so too I doubt the ability of most people to escape from some elements of a conceptual scheme which is keyed to human conduct, to moral principles or ethical rules, and to value judgments. Statements by an individual to the contrary are of little value as evidence against my generalization. We all know that actions speak far louder than words, and modern psychiatry has drawn attention to the number of mentally sick persons who seem to have difficulty in making decisions because of a conflict between their guides to action.

Among the common-sense ideas from which we cannot escape, even if we would, is our belief in the reality of other people. This conviction is the starting point for one set of ideas that are involved in making moral value judgments. We are convinced that except for minor differences, our close relatives are essentially like ourselves; they seem close duplicates in regard to what we call physical actions, thoughts, and feelings. We step both literally and figuratively on other people's toes; we hurt their feelings. This we know, because we have toes on which we can ourselves step and feelings that can be hurt. The attachment to this conviction about the close relation of ourselves to others is for most people extremely high and in origin similar to the other common-sense beliefs. It may be modified by sophistication, weakened by some types of argumentation, strengthened by some experiences. A test of the degree of attachment is suggested by the behavior of the Indian guide I mentioned in my last lecture. He vomited when he saw someone else do something that would have caused him to vomit himself. The phenomenon of nausea at the sight of human suffering is by no means rare. Such physical behavior is real testimony to the strength of the attachment of an individual to a point of view. The pain and distress of other people become to some degree our pain and distress. And except for mentally sick people, avoidance of personal pain and distress is as basic a postulate as acceptance of a three-dimensional world.

What are the minimal commitments required by a modern man to construct his philosophy of life if he be neither a religious dogmatist nor a materialistic atheist? What is the minimum number of postulates required to bring into some system the deeply imbedded assumptions about human conduct? These are questions which can hardly be answered except in terms of each individual's total experience. For if I am right, each person will have a different degree of attachment to those ideas which have been part of the Judaic-Christian tradition for generations. His rational construction of a conceptual scheme involving human beings will attempt to accommodate the presuppositions on which he really acts. Of these, his assumption of his close relation to other people, his almost physical identification with them, seems likely to be so basic as to be an essential element in a concordant scheme. For him to act as though cruelty were good in itself is no less difficult than to act as though cannibalism were good. If this be so, then a number of consequences follow that seem to lead back to the realm of spiritual values to which I have so often referred in this lecture. Time permits me to name but two.

The postulation of a sharp cleavage between animal behavior and human conduct seems essential in order to give meaning to the ideas expressed in terms of any system of spiritual evaluations. A further assumption following close on the first is that, as a minimum, the possibility may exist that our intentions and our overt actions have a relation to some large pattern of events. These would seem the minimal commitments for a modern man in the Judaic-Christian tradition who seeks to develop a philosophy of life without "jumping the fence" into the materialistic camp.

I am concerned here with the minimal commitments we seem to be driven to accept as practical men, not scientists. I am suggesting that these are imbedded in a man's total personality, much as are his beliefs in a real world, and that there is a minimal content of his ideas about what one ought and ought not to do not dissimilar to his ideas about what one ought or ought not to eat. This search is by definition a highly individual undertaking, and the results are not as uniform as those gained in the search for premises in the common-sense world of objects and other people. The results are more like the ingrained dietary beliefs to which I have already referred in these lectures. However, for people with a common cultural background, I think the basic postulates are more uniform in motivation than a verbal analysis might reveal. At all events, it seems to me worth while to attempt to formulate the minimal assumptions along the lines I have just suggested. That they represent far too small a commitment to satisfy most believing Christians, I readily admit. Yet the assumptions necessary to give meaning to the words "a universe of spiritual values" can be regarded as a common denominator among all religious faiths.

In this search for the minimal commitments, modern science can be of little or no service to modern man. Nevertheless, the benefits that flow from scientific investigations are by no means all material. Quite apart from what has been done to strengthen the hand of the Good Samaritan, science creates an atmosphere that encourages those who believe that man is not merely a social animal. The history of the last three hundred years is a record of accomplishment in the manipulation of ideas; it is a story of the flowering of the creative powers of the human mind. In the present period of reaction, in the shadow of fusion and fission bombs, we do well to stress this aspect of modern times. To have constructed a great fabric of new concepts and conceptual schemes arising from experiment and observation and fruitful beyond measure of new experiments is no small achievement. Like the Parthenon and the cathedrals of the Middle Ages, the scientific theories of the nineteenth and twentieth centuries stand as witnesses to what the human spirit can accomplish. With humility we recognize the vast oceans of our ignorance where empiricism alone can be our guide; yet we can set no limits to the future expansion of the "empire of the mind." A continued reduction in the degree of empiricism in our undertakings is both possible and of deep significance—this, in a few words, is the message that modern science brings to modern man.